Competitive Strategies
for Product Standards

Competitive Strategies for Product Standards

The strategic use of compatibility standards for competitive advantage

H. Landis Gabel

Professor of Industrial Economics
INSEAD

McGRAW-HILL BOOK COMPANY

London · New York · St Louis · San Francisco · Auckland
Bogotá · Caracas · Hamburg · Lisbon · Madrid · Mexico
Milan · Montreal · New Delhi · Panama · Paris · San Juan
São Paulo · Singapore · Sydney · Tokyo · Toronto

Published by
McGraw-Hill Book Company (UK) Limited
Shoppenhangers Road, Maidenhead, Berkshire, SL6 2QL, England
Telephone 0628 23432
Fax 0628 770224

British Library Cataloguing in Publication Data

Gabel, H. Landis
    Competitive strategies for product standards.
    1. Goods. Design
    I. Title
    658.5752
    ISBN 0-07-707315-0

Library of Congress Cataloging-in-Publication Data

Gabel, H. Landis
    Competitive strategies for product standards:
    the strategic use of compatibility standards for
    competitive advantage / H. Landis Gabel.
        p. cm.
    Includes bibliographical references and index.
    ISBN 0-07-707315-0
    1. Standardization—Case studies. 2. Commercial products—
Standards—Case studies. 3. Competition—Case studies.
4. Electronic industries—Standards—Case studies. 5. Automobile
industry and trade—Standards—Case studies. I. Title.
HD62.G33   1991
670'.218—dc20   91-11637

1234 CUP 94321

Typeset by Cambridge Composing (UK) Ltd, Cambridge
and printed and bound in Great Britain at the
University Press, Cambridge

To my family, all fully compatible

Contents

Preface

This book is the result of a number of years of thought about why products that should work together often do not do so. Those years of work, and finally this book, were precipitated by an experience I had with one of the early models of microcomputer. I remember clearly how irritated I was when I discovered that my $2500 computer would not run some software I had pirated because it had the wrong operating system—CP/M rather than MS/DOS. Thus started my education concerning operating system standards—an education that awaits readers in Chapter 2. And after buying the MS/DOS operating system, I found that I still could not run the software because the MS/DOS version for my computer was incompatible with that for IBM's PC for which the software was written. A few years later, my micro became an 'orphan'— one that was incompatible with all models then on the market. It sits unsold and unsaleable in my attic.

As is often the case, when one becomes aware of a phenomenon, one finds it is ubiquitous. Razor blades that do not fit razors, windscreen wipers that mismatch one's car model, electrical appliances that cannot be taken abroad, confusion over the placement of instruments and controls in a rented car, and video cassettes that do not match TVs are more recent personal examples of incompatibilities that have frustrated me, and surely the reader can augment this short list with his or her own examples.

Why does this occur? Is it accidental, that is, the result of independent design decisions that better coordination would have obviated? Or is it more often the result of purposeful decisions of which I and other consumers are unwitting victims? Are we necessarily victims, or are our obvious frustrations offset, at least in part, by advantages of incompatibility of which we may be unaware?

In fact most incompatibilities, like those listed above, are consciously created. So the first question to answer is what the competitive motives might be that prompt a decision to design a product that is incompatible with competitors' similar products. To address that question obviously requires that one look at the issue from the viewpoint of the producer, and thus an enquiry that started with my complaint as a consumer became a study of business strategy. The title of the book suggests the altered emphasis, although consumers as well as producers can find here some insight into the question that first perplexed me, that is, why do so many things that should work together fail to do so?

Introduction

The last decades have witnessed the rapidly growing importance of computers, telecommunications, consumer electronics, and a few similar industries in many developed countries. These industries are distinctive in terms of their high technology content, their past and prospective growth rates, their contribution to international trade, and their strategic importance. They share another characteristic as well. Each is a 'system' industry in the sense that in each, complementary products, often produced by different firms in different industries, must be compatible in order to satisfy customers' needs.

This need for compatibility between system components (like computer hardware and software) has brought to centre stage a number of strategic questions, the answers to which determine in great part the success of the firms in the competitive arena. When should a company strive to standardize product features and technologies and when should it try to avoid standardization? How can standardization best be achieved or avoided in an industy or industries comprising competitors with divergent interests? How can a firm capitalize on the potential its products or technologies have to become industry standards? Is it advantageous—and is it feasible—for competitors to agree on common 'multi-vendor' standards for their products?

All too often in the past, these and other questions relating to standards were left by default to engineers and other technical people who paid insufficient regard to their strategic importance. Now the strategic importance of standardization (or non-standardization) is rapidly gaining recognition due in good measure to the significance of the systems industries mentioned above. Yet, with this growing recognition of importance, has come an awareness that the questions are very hard to answer. The principles that are required to structure one's thinking are rarely understood, the policy choices and parameters are frequently unclear, and even worse, the terms themselves are often erroneously defined and used.

Part of the reason for this relative ignorance, especially when compared to practitioners' knowledge of other aspects of business strategy, is that these issues have not been sufficiently researched. Abstract models, business case studies, empirical studies, and pathological antitrust cases (e.g. in the photography, computer, and telecommunications industries) all exist, albeit in small numbers, and the literature is growing. Yet much more needs to be learnt, and most of what has been studied is still generally inaccessible to those who are the target of this book—those whose daily work involves making decisions that require, explicitly or implicitly, an understanding of the phenomena of standardization and competitive strategy.

This is a book on competitive strategy regarding product standards. Although the term 'standards' can be applied to many diverse product characteristics, this book is concerned with *product compatibility standards*—the kind of standards that allow different products to function together. The objective of the book is to lay out a way of thinking about standards and business strategy and to present a taxonomy of the processes and consequences of standardization. The book will make a modest attempt to describe alternative 'generic' strategies for competing on the basis of standards, but this attempt, although perhaps suggestive enough to be useful, will necessarily be imperfect given the inherent complexity of the topic. The analysis will be built around a number of illustrative case studies that are sufficiently different to cover most of the variables that are relevant to the competitive determination and implications of standards.

Chapter 1 presents to the reader the terms and concepts that will be used in the analysis of the subsequent case studies. Compatibility, standardization, gateways, network economies and externalities, natural monopoly, public goods, . . . are all terms that denote relatively precise concepts, many of which are drawn from the field of economics where they are commonly and consistently used. Yet each will be described for the layman with no prior training in economics or any other technical field. Chapter 1 concludes with a brief description of a number of strategies for exploiting the value of standards. These strategies will appear in more detail in the cases.

The four following chapters, Chapters 2 to 5, are case studies of industries in which standardization has been, or continues to be, a central competitive feature. Each chapter has two roughly equal parts. The first is the descriptive case study itself and the second is the analysis of the case.

Chapter 2 covers the microcomputer industry from its inception to the present. It is a case that demonstrates the full life cycle of a product and product standards from birth to maturity. The case demonstrates a variety of strategies regarding standards. The strategies range from strict protection of proprietary technology to *de facto* industry standardiz-ation on a single firm's technology to renewed efforts to protect proprietary technology. It is a study not only of various strategies for setting (or preventing) standards; it is also a study of the consequences of industry standardization for different types of firm in the market.

Chapter 3 is the case of video recorders (video tape recorders originally, video cassette recorders later). Like the case of microcom-puters, it covers the full life of the industry, including the long period of trial and error in the development of the technology when many efforts to set standards proved premature. The chapter addresses questions such as when standards can be set in the process of technological evolution and how many technologies and standards are appropriate, given diverse market uses of a complex product. Chapter 3 also chronicles the well-known battle between VHS and Betamax. Of particular interest is the contrast of strategies pursued by Matsushita and Sony. This battle forced the industry to convergence on a single standard (or at least one dominant standard) as had occurred in the case of microcomputers, but the process of convergence was very different in the two industries.

Chapter 4 shifts from the present to the past and from proprietary technology-based standards to public domain standards. The auto-mobile industry in the period from the turn of the century to about 1930 is the best example available of a collective effort (through the Society of Automotive Engineers) to set industry-wide standards for components and materials—an example that other industries have admired and copied. The distinguishing feature of this case is that the standards were not proprietary. Although the lack of ownership rights to standards precluded many of the strategies that appear in the other cases, standardization in automobiles faced many impediments and had a number of competitive implications that influenced firms' strategies at the time.

Chapter 5 studies the case of open standards in computers. This industry has long been a classic example of sustained competition between incompatible proprietary system standards. Yet that structure is now collapsing as the small firms in the industry, especially the European firms, come under increasing competitive pressure. It is their hope to replace the existing structure with one of open (i.e. non-proprietary) collective standards to 'level the playing field' on which they compete with larger firms. Yet in no other case of comparable significance has a group of firms succeeded in setting open standards in a high technology industry. Only the passage of time will tell if it is possible here, but our analysis leads to a pessimistic forecast.

The final chapter presents a set of hypotheses induced from the case studies and buttressed by the findings of formal modelling that have appeared in the academic literature and to which reference is made. The hypotheses deal with two broad issues: one is the setting of standards and the other is the consequences of industry-wide standardization.

1. The basics

Introduction
The objective of this chapter is to define the terms and concepts that will be needed for the case studies that follow and to begin to assemble the pieces required to analyse product compatibility standards and competitive strategy.

Product compatibility
At the most basic level, our definition of *compatibility* between products is the same as the layman's—compatible products somehow 'go together'. One aspect of this 'going together' is what an economist would call a *complementarity* in consumption. If two products are complements in consumption, an increase in the consumption of one will cause an increase in the consumption of the other.[1] Textbook examples of complementary products include tea and lemon, cars and petrol, and cameras and film.

Tea and lemon are complementary products, but they are not the focus of this book. Our focus is uniquely on those complementary products that must be *consciously made* to go together. Thus, while the example of tea and lemon is not relevant to us, that of cameras and film is. So are car engines and petrol octane numbers, railway wagons and track gauges, nut and bolt threads, rifles and cartridges, and electrical plugs and sockets. In each case, the products are complementary, and in addition, they must be consciously designed (or possibly adapted) to function together, that is, to be compatible. This need for a conscious decision throws the issue of product compatibility into the realm of business strategy, for often firms may prefer to design products so that they do *not* go together. Much of this book is about the choice of compatibility or incompatibility.

Although a camera and film is a good example of the kind of product that will be discussed in this book, our concept of compatibility goes beyond pairs of physical products. Compatibility can also exist between physical products and human knowledge. A typist's skill can be compatible (or incompatible) with a typewriter keyboard, a computer programmer's knowledge with a computer language, and a pilot's expertise with the layout of an aircraft's cockpit controls.

1

Dimensions and degrees of compatibility

If compatibility were one-dimensional and dichotomous (i.e. if products were simply compatible or incompatible), the analytics would be relatively simple. Unfortunately, compatibility usually exists in different dimensions and degrees.

In our subsequent case studies, we will have occasion to distinguish two dimensions of compatibility. The first is *multi-vendor compatibility*. This implies compatibility between different producers' models of a product. This compatibility can be direct, as with different vendors' telecommunications equipment for example. Or it can be indirect. Canon and Nikon cameras can be said to be compatible not because they work with each other but because each is compatible with the same complementary products.[2] Both use 35 mm film and have the same lens mounting. IBM and Compaq microcomputers and Thompson and Matsushita VHS-format VCRs are other examples.

The second dimension of compatibility is *multi-vintage compatibility*. This implies that successive generations of a product are compatible with each other or with a common set of complements. An example drawn from one of the cases that follow is the compatibility between IBM's PC and its later PS/2. (As will be seen, these two vintages of microcomputer were nearly but not perfectly compatible.)

This distinction between multi-vendor and multi-vintage compatibility will prove to be important, especially in instances when firms contemplate converting from one standard to another. This can occur on the occasion of a merger between two competitors with different and incompatible product standards. And it can occur when a group of firms with incompatible standards determines to adopt a single multi-vendor standard. In either case, some firms will face a costly process of adapting or scrapping products that complement the standards being abandoned. In instances like this, multi-vendor compatibility may only be possible at the sacrifice of multi-vintage compatibility.

Not only is compatibility a multi-dimensional product attribute, but it may exist in different *degrees of functionality*—or at different quality levels—along either dimension. In computers, these degrees of compatibility follow a hierarchy from file transfer (the lowest degree of compatibility) to plug compatibility (the highest degree). In the various telecommunications standards, there are also degrees (called 'layers') of increasingly complete and complex standards. Multi-vendor and multi-vintage compatibility may occur to any one of these degrees. Generally, a low degree of compatibility is relatively easily achieved but can imply

2

substantial consumer frustration with 'complementary' products that do not work. A high degree, by contrast, is likely to be expensive because it can only be achieved by reducing product functionality or flexibility. This trade-off is particularly evident in the design of a new vintage of product. There is a common tension between the objective to introduce the most advanced—albeit incompatible—technology and an objective to ensure multi-vintage compatibility—an objective that limits design freedom. The common result is an imperfect degree of compatibility.

Product standardization, standards networks, and installed bases

Product compatibility is not synonymous with product *standardization*. Compatibility is a relational attribute between products, that is, they 'go together'. Standardization is a *particular way* of making products go together. Standardized products go together because they have been designed in conformance with a common technical specification—the standard.[3]

Groups of products, which have been designed to go together by common reference to a design standard, are said to belong to the same *network*. Thus, there is a network of 110 volt appliances all of which can be plugged into the standard two-pronged socket familiar to Americans. There is another network of 220 volt appliances that is familiar to the French. These two networks are incompatible. That is, a 110 volt appliance will not function with a 220 volt electrical supply. Similarly, there are many different rifles made by many different firms, all of which fire a 22-calibre cartridge. And there are many different 22-calibre cartridges available on the market, differing by bullet weight, shape, and quantity of powder. All belong to the same network, however, since all can work together, and the network encompasses both multi-vendor and multi-vintage standardized products. The 22-calibre network is, however, incompatible with the 30-calibre network, the 12-gauge network, etc.

The stock of capital that is compatible with a specific standard and which thus belongs to the standard's network is called the standard's *installed base*. This installed base is often comprised of physical capital (all 110 volt appliances, the houses so wired, the generating facilities, etc.), but as noted above, it may also entail human capital. A computer programmer may have invested in learning BASIC, and his or her knowledge of BASIC is part of the BASIC programming language's installed base.

From the viewpoint of the consumer, networks with large installed

3

bases are generally preferable to those with small installed bases, all other things being equal. The VHS standard for video cassette recorders is more attractive now than the Betamax standard because there are more VHS machines to choose from in the stores and more VHS-format films in the rental shops.

The benefits of networks with large installed bases are commonly called *network economies,* and they are proportional to the size of the installed base.[4] These network economies derive from economies of scale in production, distribution, and service and the spreading of fixed research and development costs over a larger sales volume. Network economies will lower costs, and by increasing the return on investment in complementary products, they may increase the variety of complements on the market. Another form of network economy is direct communication (as in telecommunications) or the sharing of complementary products between network members as occurs in the VCR market. Finally, there are network economies that will come from industrial restructuring, which will be described in a number of the cases that follow in subsequent chapters.

In many respects, network economies are analytically similar to economies of experience (i.e. the 'learning curve'). Both are functions of cumulative output. But there are some important differences. Unlike economies of experience, network economies are not necessarily firm-specific. Many different firms may produce products for the same network and share common network economies. Furthermore, economies of experience depend only on actual cumulative output. In the case of network economies, expectations of future network size may be equally or more important because these expectations may influence consumer and producer behaviour. This implies an important role for business to shape what are likely to be self-fulfilling expectations.

Although it is difficult to estimate the absolute size of network economies,[5] they will increase with an increase in production economies of scale, in research and development costs, or in any other fixed costs associated with a technological vintage. By contrast, relative network economies will diminish to the extent that it is inexpensive to convert complements from one network to another network. For example, inexpensive transcription of a film from a VHS to a Betamax video cassette implies relatively low network economies in the VCR industry. The very high cost of transcribing major software applications programs from one mainframe computer operating system to another causes network economies to be large in that industry.

Gateways between standards

Networks of different standards are invariably observed wherever there is to be compatibility. But standardization is not the only way of creating compatibility. If there are several different incompatible standards' networks in existence, it may be possible to link them by means of a *gateway*.

One common gateway is via the production of *multi-standard* products. Three speed (33/45/78 r.p.m.) phonograph turntables, PAL/SECAM/NTSC multi-standard television receivers and VCRs, and dual (8- and 16-bit) chip microcomputers are examples. Whether it is economical to sell multi-standard products depends on the technologies in question. Only recently, for example, with the introduction of electronic typewriters, has it become feasible to switch easily between QWERTY and Dvorak keyboard standards.

Adaptors represent another common gateway technology. In the computer industry, special software can often translate between different standards. These gateways are frequently produced for the open market by independent software vendors or value-added resellers. A plug adaptor, which allows electrical appliances to be used in different countries, is another example. In contrast to multi-standard equipment, the sale of adaptors is not tied to the sale of the product by its producer but is normally purchased separately and often from a different supplier. Adaptors are a common method of producing compatibility when there are several standards that a random consumer may want to integrate, when a new standard would otherwise make existing installed bases obsolete, and when producers' strategies to keep their standards' networks incompatible create a market for an adaptor that the producers cannot suppress.

The feasibility of gateways depends on the degree of compatibility between networks. Electrical appliances in the United Kingdom cannot be used in France because the plug prongs have different shapes. Yet since both countries use 220 volt electrical supply, it is a relatively simple operation to use a plug adaptor when travelling from one country to the other. The same is not possible going from the United Kingdom to the United States, however, because the voltage differs, and this requires a more expensive adaptor—a voltage transformer.

Gateways suffer as a technology to produce compatibility when there are many different standards' networks that must be linked, since a different gateway is required for each pairing. Linking 4 networks requires 6 gateways; linking 10 requires 45 separate gateways.

A simple way to illustrate many of the concepts that have been described above is to consider the example of natural languages—English, French, etc. Individuals have a demand to communicate, that is, a demand for compatibility of spoken and written symbols. Different linguistic standards exist (defined by specifications laid out in dictionaries and grammar texts), each providing compatibility within its own networks of users but not between users in different networks. The users—English and French speakers, for example—benefit from this compatibility within their respective language networks, and the benefit is roughly proportional to the size of the network. (In this sense, English speakers are better off than French speakers.) To benefit from membership of a standard network, users must invest in learning the language. This investment creates the installed base of capital ('human capital', in this example) that is compatible with the standard. A simple picture of this is shown in Fig. 1.1.

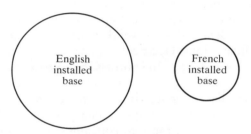

Figure 1.1 Separate linguistic networks

Suppose (not unrealistically) that because of improvements in transportation and communication technologies, there were to be a demand for more compatibility between nations with different languages. How can it be met by increased supply?

One way is by greater standardization. With competition between the networks, one might expand at the expense of others. For example, English could slowly displace French as the existing installed base if French depreciated via demographic change (Fig. 1.2).

Alternatively, new 'markets' could adopt one language as their standard. An example that comes to mind is the case of air traffic control where English has been chosen as a common world-wide standard. Alternatively, a new standard language like Esperanto could displace several existing languages (see Fig. 1.3).

Either the expansion of one existing standard at the expense of others

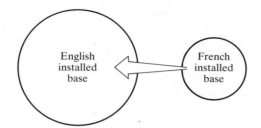

Figure 1.2   Standardization by network competition

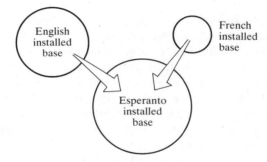

Figure 1.3   Agreement on a 'neutral' standard

or the adoption of a new standard to replace several existing ones can increase compatibility. But note that they are quite different both in their absolute costs and in their distributive effects. Convergence to the largest network (presumably English in the example chosen) minimizes the cost of converting the installed base, but it disadvantages French speakers to the benefit of English speakers. That is, it is not competitively neutral. Common adoption of a new language (e.g. Esperanto) is more costly since all the installed bases must be converted. It is competitively neutral, however. This trade-off between efficiency and equity will appear as an issue in several of the cases in this book, particularly the case of open system standards in computers. We will see that voluntary open standards agreements are likely to settle on the equitable selection of a neutral but costly new standard, while market competition between standards will more likely cause convergence to an efficient but non-neutral existing standard.

Increased standardization is not the only way to increase compatibility, however. Compatibility can also be produced by gateways (Fig.

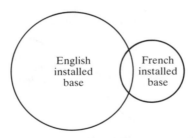

Figure 1.4   Compatibility by gateways

1.4). For example, individuals can learn several languages (analogous to a multi-standard TV or phonograph player). Another possibility is to use professional translators to link linguistic networks (like using software to convert an application program from one computer operating system to another as will be seen repeatedly in subsequent chapters).

Clearly, each alternative way of producing compatibility is costly although the nature of the cost is quite different. One aspect of the cost of standardization, about which much will be made in the case studies, is the loss of variety. Would the world suffer a loss if English replaced the myriad of different languages that now exist? Is there a value to their variety? (Presumably the French would think so.) What about computer languages?

These different ways of producing compatibility are essentially competitors, each with unique economic characteristics both in terms of its production and in terms of the utility it affords consumers. To anticipate much that will follow, some produce compatibility for collective consumption while others do not. Some restrict the variety of product offerings on the market more than others. Some require customers to scrap the existing installed base and others do not. Some integrate networks on the demand side but not on the supply side while others do the reverse.

A final significance of the different ways of producing compatibility is that they are commonly offered by different types of firms. Large integrated system producers may make strategic decisions on standardization or non-standardization. But to produce a single conversion package that allows members of one network to join another may not require the size, broad product line, manufacturing expertise, control of distribution channels, or any of the other competitive advantages that major integrated systems producers presumably possess. That is, entry

8

barriers may be very low in the market for adaptors making it possible for small firms to thwart the competitive strategies of large standardized systems' producers.

Network economies and natural monopoly

Network economies, their relationship to network size, and the feasibility of gateways are important because they determine whether a network is a *natural monopoly*. If network economies are large, if they decline slowly with increased network size up to the size of the total market, and if gateways are not feasible, then it will be efficient to have only one network. One network will be a natural monopoly in the dual sense that it is efficient that only one should exist, and that its sole existence will be a natural market outcome. If two or more incompatible networks are competing in an undifferentiated market, then there will be strong pressure favouring the relatively larger to the point that it will displace the smaller. This positive feedback will result in increased concentration, and ultimately monopoly, of the standard in a fashion similar to that with production economies of scale or economies of experience. On the other hand, if network economies reach effective limits short of the size of the entire market, or if gateways can be made, inter-standards competition is feasible with little loss of efficiency.

Standards are in this respect like discothèques. Individuals prefer to go where there are lots of others.[6] They benefit from the presence of others, and between two rival discos they would tend to choose the relatively more crowded—making it more crowded yet. If the two discos were undifferentiated (by style of music, age of clientele, location, etc.), only one would survive competition unless, perhaps, the size of the potential market exceeded its capacity.

Network externalities

Much of the economic benefit of an incremental increase in network size does not accrue to the incremental network member but is shared by all existing members of the network. For example, an individual who installs a telephone will receive some of the benefit—he or she can communicate with others on the network. But there are further benefits that accrue automatically to the other network members. They can now communicate in return. Since the decision to join the telephone network is based on personal rather than collective costs and benefits, there is an *externality* in the market (i.e. some benefit falls externally to the decision maker) and an inadequate incentive for individuals to join the network.

9

Again, standards resemble discos. Each new member experiences a personal benefit from membership, but in addition, each new member also benefits all existing members. Disco managers understand the significance of this externality very well, and they commonly provide a financial incentive for new members, especially early in the disco's life and especially for women (for whom the externality is presumably greatest). We will see that there are some very clear strategy analogies with regard to setting standards.

The literature generally associates these network economies (external or otherwise) with standardization, but many are not unique to it. The producer of a TV programme does not care whether the network that can be reached has been achieved by a single industry-wide standard or by multi-standard sets. On the other hand, the economics of TV set production are very sensitive to the difference between a common standard and multi-standard gateway.

Intellectual property, public goods, and free riders

A standard is *intellectual property* (i.e. it is not a tangible product) and like all intellectual property it is a *public good*. A public good is a good or service with the property that provision for one consumer automatically could entail provision for others at no additional social cost, that is, consumption is not rival. Examples include mathematical theorems, musical scores, literature, etc.[7] Once a standard is set, it may be possible for firms that did not support its creation to use it at no cost to society. If enough firms try to be 'free riders', there will be insufficient investment in standardization. This problem does not exist in the case of most conversion technologies because the firm that invests in the technology can generally appropriate the full rewards.[8] All things being equal, this externality creates a bias against standardization in the market for compatibility. Of course, the firms that do invest in standards may try to exclude free riders from using 'their' standards without paying for them. This, in turn, raises a number of other important issues concerning the supply of standardization, which will be discussed in the case studies.

Property rights and alternative ways of setting standards

A standard can be *proprietary* or in the *public domain*, implying respectively the presence or absence of a *private property right* to the standard. Whether a standard is proprietary or public is a legal question. Computer programs and microprocessor chips are afforded legal protec-

10

tion against unauthorized copying. The sizing of toilet paper rolls and dispensers is not. In general, proprietary standards are common in circumstances in which the establishment of standards requires a significant investment. Since standards are public goods, that investment would not take place in the absence of legal protection against unauthorized copying. Because they are expensive to create, technical standards are usually proprietary. By contrast, dimensional standards, which require nothing more than common agreement between firms, are usually in the public domain.

Proprietary standards can in turn be *restricted* or *open*, implying respectively that the owner does or does not restrict other firms from producing compatible products, that is, from joining the network. Whether a standard is restricted or open is its owner's decision to make.

An open proprietary standard is similar in many ways to a public domain standard, but there are some important differences. For one thing, the owner of a proprietary standard usually retains the right and responsibility to maintain and upgrade the standard. For another, the owner may choose to restrict a formerly open standard and in one way or another exploit those who became locked into the standard. This is a risk that faces adoptors of an open proprietary standard but that does not exist in the case of a public standard. Of course, restriction is usually a question of degree. Intellectual property is notoriously costly to protect, and the owner's decision is more accurately one of determining how much restriction to attempt. Assuming that other firms want to produce compatible products, perfect restriction will rarely be possible, let alone optimal.

The definitions above allow one to categorize alternative means of supplying and competing with standards in a matrix as drawn in Fig. 1.5. Quadrants 1 and 2 are each recognizable strategies for exploiting a proprietary standard's potential while quadrant 4 describes voluntary industry standardization around a standard that is not controlled by any single firm. (Quadrant 3 is irrelevant since it is not possible to restrict access to a public domain standard.)

Restricted access to proprietary standards and rent maximization

If one assumes that proprietary rights exist for standards—which is the case in most high technology industries—the first question to consider is how the owners of the rights can maximize what can be earned from them. There are only a few ways by which this can be done. The most obvious is to make the standards scarce by restricting access to them

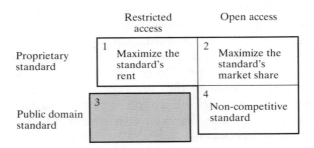

Figure 1.5   Types and strategies of standards

and thus earn profits (more precisely, 'scarcity rents') from them. This is quadrant 1 in Fig. 1.5. There are two broad strategies to extract these rents. One is to deny any other producer use of the standard and to sell a full system, that is, a full set of compatible elements, at a monopoly price. The other is to licence the standard to other firms.

THE FULL SYSTEM MONOPOLY

Competitors can be denied access to a proprietary standard by patent or copyright protection. The owner can then exploit the standard by integrating horizontally and/or vertically to produce and sell the full system of compatible products and complements, frequently bundled together, at a monopoly price.

This strategy is commonly associated with the integrated computer manufacturers and their mainframe computer systems, as will be described in Chapter 5. Each firm has its own proprietary system standard (which is incompatible with those of other producers), and each produces a broad range of hardware and software products that are usually multi-vintage compatible.

The conventional wisdom is that this is a highly profitable strategy, especially if a producer can lock customers into its network by virtue of their need for multi-vintage compatibility. Over time, the trap becomes ever tighter as the size of the customers' installed base grows. With ever-rising switching costs (and thus falling price elasticity of demand), the profit-maximizing monopoly price rises.

A more subtle virtue of the full line monopoly strategy is that it may make a second-best form of price discrimination possible. The principles underlying the use of a tied product to meter demand and extract consumer surplus, such as in the automobile spare parts business or in camera film sales, will not be covered here, although they are discussed in Chapter 4. This strategy has faced a number of successful legal challenges, however,[9] and, of course, it is only practical when the firm sells the metering complement.

Although the full system monopoly strategy may look attractive, it suffers from many problems. The first is that the firm is obliged to offer a full line of complements. This may be financially burdensome, especially early in a product's life cycle when the network is small and initial research and development costs are amortized over few sales. But that is not the only problem. In addition, the firm may not be efficient in producing the full line of products and may find itself (possibly unconsciously) dissipating its profit by subsidizing inefficient internal operations. Organizational barriers may soon inhibit subcontracting even if the company becomes aware of the inefficiency. Much of this describes the experiences of some of the smaller European computer firms who earn modest rents from captured customers but then dissipate those rents by cross-subsidizing inefficient in-house manufacturing.

A way of reducing the initial financial burden of this strategy is to enlist support from other firms. For example, a computer manufacturer may try to exclude other hardware manufacturers from its standard, while simultaneously encouraging independent software vendors to develop applications packages to supplement those produced by the manufacturer itself. But the more open is the standard to outside producers of complements, the more open it is likely to be to copying by competitors.

A second problem is that the network of the standard may be relatively small. A small network normally implies that the range of complementary products will be small and possibly expensive, thus limiting the demand from which rents are to be extracted. The firm can try to mitigate the problem by heavy investment in the complementary products in the hope that doing so will 'bootstrap' the standard, but this will be extremely expensive. Of course, if the standard is dominant in the market, as IBM's standards have traditionally been in the computer industry, the problem will not be severe, but few firms start in such an attractive position.

A third problem is that the strategy assumes that a standard's monopoly will be profitable. Yet the existence of a monopoly does not guarantee its profitable exploitation. In a market of several incompatible standards, competition is similar to that for monopoly franchises (or

13

the competition between discos). Different producers compete for positions as the sole long-term suppliers of specific customers who become tied to their monopolist suppliers by the installed base. If there are many suppliers and if it is feasible to specify *ex ante* the supply conditions, these sole-supply relationships would entail no opportunity to earn rents. The rents are bid away in the initial competition for each customer's business.

In the case of standards, this 'franchise competition' is likely to be extremely intense, especially early in a product's life cycle. These are the conditions in which the forces that push many standards towards few are strongest. Early market success and market share gains will be self-reinforcing, partly because consumers will jump on to the bandwagon and partly because independent producers of complementary products will want to invest in the likely market share winner. The result will be a self-fulfilling prophecy. This provides a strong motive for penetration pricing (and possibly even predatory pricing). Because the success of a standard in establishing itself in the marketplace is heavily dependent on consumers' expectations of the size of the standard's future network, advertising and promotional expenses will be important and heavy. All this means that positive cash flows will be far off even for the firm that eventually succeeds. For the firms that fail, the financial losses can be catastrophic. For example, RCA Victor spent several million dollars in the first year of its unsuccessful effort to coax a reluctant industry to adopt its 45 r.p.m. standard in lieu of Columbia's 33 r.p.m. standard.

Even the firm that eventually succeeds in establishing and exploiting a major monopoly position is vulnerable to the counterstrategies of its competitors and others. One counterstrategy is to develop a gateway that releases locked-in customers who are unlikely to get trapped twice. A second counterstrategy for competitors is to counterfeit the standard. This is almost always possible to some degree, and the higher the monopoly price that the standard's owner charges, the greater is the willingness of both consumers and other producers to buy and sell possibly inexact copies of the standard.

LICENSING THE STANDARD

In contrast to a strategy of exploiting a proprietary standard by integration and exclusion of other firms, the owner of the standard can license other firms to produce the full range of compatible products, possibly even in competition with the owner's product line. Licensing can be literal—charging a royalty for use of the technology—or it can be by analogy. The standard can be embedded in a hardware component (such as in a computer chip or the recording head of a VCR) which is then sold at a margin equivalent to a licence fee.

This strategy has two extreme variants that depend on the approach that the firm takes to the licence fee. At one extreme, the owner can set the profit-maximizing royalty with no regard to its effect on its own share of the market for the products embodying the standard. This is the case discussed here. The alternative approach—to charge a low royalty or even to license the standard freely in order to maximize its market share—will be discussed below. With a profit-maximizing royalty, all the firm's rents will be earned directly from the standard, and any other activities of the firm (e.g. manufacturing) will be conducted at arm's length. The firm can be regarded as a monopolist with respect to the standard but possibly as a perfect competitor with respect to all its other activities. In fact, whether the firm does anything but collect licence fees is analytically irrelevant.

Obviously, the challenge to the firm is to find a standard with a high market value. Little can be said here about how to do this. Irrespective of the value of the standard, however, this strategy has the virtue that the various activities of the firm must earn their own way, and there will be no possibility that counter-productive cross-subsidies will dissipate profits.

OPEN PROPRIETARY STANDARDS AND MARKET SHARE MAXIMIZATION
Instead of making the standard scarce in order to earn a rent from it, the owner can open access to the standard by setting a low or neglible royalty with the specific intent of attracting other competitors to adopt the standard, thus expanding the standard's network to the point where it becomes the *de facto* industry standard. This is quadrant 2 in Fig. 1.5. The convergence of competing standards in the market will be much quicker to the extent that firms compete in this fashion. The obvious question, however, is how a rent is then to be earned. By definition, little or none comes directly from the standard since it is not scarce. Because the answer is not obvious, a frequent hypothesis in the literature of standardization is that a dominant firm will oppose industry standardization. Yet this is not always the case as the following chapters will show.

One circumstance in which this strategy can be profitable is when the firm has other competitive strengths or scarce rent-earning assets that the standard complements. For example, the firm may be a low cost producer or it may have patents or specialized know-how in the host of

15

complementary products that are distinct from the standard itself. Matsushita is a low cost manufacturer that inexpensively licenses its VHS standard in the VCR industry hoping to earn an efficiency rent on large-scale production of the standardized product. Xerox charges only a token royalty for its local area network standard, Ethernet, presumably to capitalize on the firm's competitive advantage producing and marketing equipment that attaches to the network.

The risk with this strategy is that the firm may find its envisioned competitive strength illusory. Firms that have long protected themselves from competition by restricting access to their standard may easily overestimate their competitiveness outside of a protected market. The story of IBM's PC, recounted in the next chapter, is a good example. The product was remarkable for its open architecture. Irrespective of how IBM hoped to profit from the PC, it found that it was unable to hold back the many invaders of the standard. Despite its extreme efforts to be cost competitive, including uncharacteristic external sourcing of major components, IBM has found itself a relatively high cost producer and it lost margins and market share. IBM had an unexpected experience as well in the 1960s when it opened its standards for the System 360 (recounted in Chapter 5).

As a final point, it may be possible to combine open and restricted standards. A firm may freely license a proprietary standard to establish its dominance in the market and then exploit a first-mover advantage as the technology evolves. Alternatively, it may try to restrict its open standard once it becomes the *de facto* industry standard. IBM provides examples of both possibilities. The European Community antitrust case against IBM was settled in 1984 in part by IBM's agreement to release information on its technologies early enough to reduce the first-mover advantage from which it was alleged to profit. And the trade press speculated for a number of years that IBM would capitalize on the dominance of the open PC standards by closing them. (It never did.)

INDUSTRY COOPERATION ON A PUBLIC STANDARD

An industry-wide *de facto* standard could be an outcome of inter-standards competition as has been seen, but this would not normally be called a 'cooperative' outcome. Truly cooperative industry-wide agreement on a public domain standard—quadrant 4 in Fig. 1.5—is very different from the competitive processes that have been discussed above. The principal reasons have to do with both the process and its consequences. If a standard is in the public domain, none of the

16

competitive strategies described above are possible, and there is little basis for competition with respect to the standard.

Examples of public industry standards include machine screw threads, car tyre sizes, widths and depths of refrigerators, the relative positions of car foot controls, farm equipment hitches, and paper and envelope sizes. The characteristic feature of these examples and of most public domain standards is that they are dimensions with no legally enforced property rights. Thus, the standards *per se* cannot earn rents because they cannot be made scarce. (Public domain standards are the topic of Chapter 4.)

Although the stereotypic cases of industry-wide public domain standards are dimensions, such cases are not very fashionable compared to those in which standards involve sophisticated technologies and intellectual property. Is it not possible, however, for firms to cooperate in developing costly technological standards for the public domain? This is a case that will be the focus of Chapter 5.

The main problem one confronts in this case is the public goods character of standards. If enough firms try to be free riders, there will be no investment and no standard.

There are ways out of the free rider trap, however. Concentrated industries may be able to agree on an equitable sharing of the burden, and empirical studies have confirmed that voluntary standards are most common in such industries.[10] Industry trade associations, to which all or most industry members belong and contribute, often support public goods' production, standards included. Tax-supported national standards' bodies perform some of this work as do government financed research laboratories or grants to industry. Open Systems Interconnection (OSI) and Integrated Services Digital Network (ISDN) standards are examples. Sometimes it is possible that very large buyers can push vendors into open standards as seems to be the case with the Manufacturing Automation Protocol (MAP) standard, a manufacturing standard promulgated by GM, Boeing, and other huge firms. None the less, with the exception of cases in which there is a significant government involvement, costly high technology standards in the public domain, that is, truly non-competitive private sector cooperation in setting technology standards, is extremely rare.

Notes and references

1. The precise definition of complements is that an increase in the price of one good will reduce the consumption of the other.
2. A distinction is sometimes made between direct 'peer-to-peer compatibility' that links functionally identical products (like telephones) and indirect

'interface compatibility' which links complementary products (like cameras and film).

3. We will be concerned throughout this book with product compatibility standards. There are, however, other kinds of standards that serve other purposes. For example, monetary standards (the dollar, the lira, etc.) and measurement standards (metre, litre, etc.) serve as counting units. Quality standards exist (in the areas of consumer and workplace safety, environmental protection, etc.) for legal or regulatory reasons. And standards are often set to reduce variety as in the case of standardized shirt or shoe sizes. One should note that the distinctions between these different kinds of standards are not always precise. For example, car tyre size standards exist both to reduce variety and to ensure compatibility with wheel rims.

4. The nature of network economies is discussed in most of the economics literature on standards. See, for example, Braunstein, Y. and L. White, Setting technical compatibility standards: an economic analysis, *Antitrust Bulletin*, Summer 1985; Carlton, D., and J. M. Klamer, The need for coordination among firms, with special reference to network industries, *University of Chicago Law Review*, 50, Spring 1983; Dybvig, P. and C. Spatt, Adoption externalities as public goods', *Journal of Public Economics*, 20, 1983; Hemenway, D., *Industrywide Voluntary Product Standards*, Ballinger, Cambridge, Mass., 1975; and Kindelberger, C., Standards as public, collective and private goods, *Kyklos*, 36 (3), 1983.

5. It is difficult to generalize about the character and extent of network economies, and there is little specific empirical estimation of them. The voluminous testimony in the US antitrust case against IBM did not include any estimate for the computer industry, although G. Brock (*The US Computer Industry: A study in market power*, Ballinger, Cambridge, Mass., 1975) estimated that a firm with 10 per cent of the market would suffer software costs 50 per cent higher than a firm with a 100 per cent monopoly. As another example, Philips estimated in 1984 that it could save $175 million annually in production if television standards were uniform in the European Community.

6. In technical terms, discos and standards exhibit increasing returns to scale. More will be made of this in the case studies.

7. Note that this definition holds even if non-payers are excluded by law from the consumption of public goods.

8. For example, the cost of the extra components is intrinsic to the price of multi-standard products.

9. For example, it was an issue in *International Business Machines Corp.* v. *US*, (1962). For further discussion, see Scherer, F. M., *Industrial Market Structure and Economic Performance*, 2nd ed. Rand McNally, Chicago, 1980, pp. 582–4.

10. See Lecraw, D., 'Some economic effects of standards', *Applied Economics*, August 1984; and Link, A., 'Market structure and voluntary product standards', *Applied Economics*, June 1983.

2. The case of microcomputers

A CASE STUDY

Introduction

The microcomputer industry was born only in the last decade and a half and since then has passed through two and into a third generation. In this brief period, it has progressed from a novelty only suited to an engineer or sophisticated hobbyist to a business necessity and a common household possession. From a totally unstandardized heap of wires and electronic components that the owner had to assemble, the microcomputer practically became a standardized commodity. The process of *de facto* standardization occurred almost exclusively from the widespread adoption of popular designs and components available on the open market, rather than from formal inter-firm agreement. Now, standards are again in turmoil.

In its brief history, the industry has witnessed virtually every competitive strategy and situation that is generic to technological standards. This makes the microcomputer industry one of the best case studies of the competitive use of standards.

The beginnings of the industry: 1975–81

The first period in the short history of the microcomputer[1] runs from its first appearance in 1975 to IBM's introduction of its PC in 1981.[2] This period is distinguished from later periods by the electronics technology, by the lack of a significant industry-wide standard, and by the still small market that, while growing rapidly, was yet to experience the explosive growth that would accompany the era of the PC.

The origins of the microcomputer can be traced to the early 1970s and the development of the microprocessor by Intel Corporation.[3] The first commercial microcomputer, the *Altair 8800*, was introduced as a kit selling for $395 by a small US firm, MITS, in 1975. Its core was an 8-bit Intel microprocessor, the 8080.[4] Although certainly a microcomputer, this machine (and the others that immediately followed it on the market) not only had to be assembled by its owner but also had to be

19

programmed by the owner in machine language.[5] All of this rendered it useful only to technically sophisticated users.

The first complete microcomputer systems—systems requiring no soldering, wiring, or programming—appeared in 1976 and 1977 and included the Tandy TRS-80 (selling for $499), Commodore PET (priced at $495), and Apple II (selling for about $1200). These systems, typical of the first generation microcomputers, included a keyboard, an 8-bit microprocessor, memory, keyboard, and some form of output device, commonly the user's TV. They also came with an operating system,[6] and applications software[7] was either provided with the machine or was available for purchase separately. In any case, users no longer had to be expert programmers. Not only did this make microcomputers useful to individuals with no technical ability, it also gave birth to the microcomputer software industry.

Most microcomputer manufacturers did (and still do) little more than assemble purchased elements of the system. These elements included the operating systems and applications software, the microprocessors and other electronic devices, and peripheral products like keyboards and printers.

Of these various elements, the two most important to the producer were the operating system and the microprocessor that ran it. Since they were so frequently purchased from independent firms, some modest *de facto* standardization began to emerge for both by the late 1970s. Perhaps the most important software to be used by a number of different firms was the CP/M operating system, a 1974 proprietary development of Digital Research Corporation.[8] CP/M was adopted by Commodore, Hewlett-Packard, Osborne, Zenith, and others, and it was used with several different 'standard' microprocessors including the Mostek 6502 (the chip the Apple II used), the Zilog Z-80 (used in the TR-80), and the Intel 8085.

CP/M was used on more than 50 different microcomputer models, but its share of the operating system market was modest (20–30 per cent around 1980) because the two largest micro manufacturers used their own proprietary alternatives. The Apple II's operating system, Apple/DOS, and Tandy's TRS-80's operating system, TRS/DOS,[9] were proprietary developments, and neither was ever licensed to any other firm.

Beyond using their own proprietary operating systems, Apple and Tandy chose sharply different strategies—strategies that would reappear throughout the history of the industry. Apple chose what is

20

called 'open architecture' for its products, while Tandy chose to restrict independent firms' access to its technology.

Apple's strategy of open architecture—an innovative one at the time—implied releasing all the technical information necessary for independent firms to produce complementary products. Of particular interest to Apple was independent firms' software development for the Apple II. Although Apple had software development capability (the firm had written Apple/DOS), it foresaw a significant competitive advantage in a large repertoire of applications (in particular, of games) that the company did not have the internal resources to create.[10] One element of the company's strategy was to advertise in computer and electronic publications for submissions of programs from independent writers that could be run on the Apple II. Hardware was also important. Apple introduced the now-ubiquitous 5.25-inch floppy disk with its Apple II. This storage medium made it possible for the independent software firms to market programs in a more convenient form than tape cassettes that floppies replaced. And the Apple II had empty slots in its cabinet that could accommodate microprocessor boards made by Apple or others to enhance the machine's performance. For example, one such board, the Microsoft Z-80, allowed the Apple II to run programs written for the Z-80 chip and the CP/M operating system. That is, the Z-80 'gateway' allowed the Apple II to mimic a CP/M machine.

In contrast to Apple, Tandy chose not to release technical information to the public. As a consequence, Tandy had to develop all the applications software to run on its proprietary operating system, and Tandy customers had to invest in software that could never run on any other hardware.

Despite the fact that the Apple II used an operating system differing from the loosely defined industry standard (CP/M), it was extremely popular. This popularity was due to the quality of its video display and to the demand created by a spreadsheet program called VisiCalc, written by Personal Software[11] specifically for the Apple II. More than 300 000 copies of VisiCalc were sold between its introduction in 1979 and 1982. Other popular programs included Microsoft's BASIC (versions of which were made for virtually all micros), and a database management program from Ashton-Tate named dBase II. The Apple II's early popularity in turn generated so much support from independent software firms that, by the early 1980s, it had an installed base of 15 000–16 000 applications programs which exceeded that of any

21

other microcomputer. Its 1981 sales of 171 000 units made it the most popular micro model on the market.

Although the Apple II had the largest library of software, CP/M's repertoire in the early 1980s was also extensive, driven by the approximately 250 000 installations on more than 50 different makes of computer. Independent firms developed popular applications programs like MicroPro's WordStar, the best selling word processing program as late as 1984.

By the end of this first period in the industry's life, approximately 150 companies had sold more than half a million microcomputers. The early leaders, Apple, Tandy, and Commodore, maintained their leadership through the period. Apple was first with over 20 per cent of the world market in 1981. Tandy was second with about 15 per cent of the market. Commodore had 7 per cent. The world-wide hardware market was worth about $3000 million.

IBM's PC: Open standards in the industry

With its introduction of the PC—and its entry into the microcomputer industry—in August 1981, IBM inaugurated the second stage in the industry's history. From cumulative sales of a little more than half a million units by 1981, the industry would ship 20 million PCs and PC clones by the time the next generation of equipment was on the market. Microcomputers would become *de rigueur* in the business office. The technology would undergo a significant improvement in the jump to 16-bit processing. Standardization would become the rule rather than the exception. And by the middle of the 1980s, compatibility between micro models and with huge installed bases of software and peripheral products would become the principal competitive issue in the industry.

IBM was conspicuous for its absence from the microcomputer industry in the decade of the 1970s. This absence led the company into a crash program to launch a microcomputer in the beginning of the 1980s. The program was organized in 1980 as an independent business (what Chairman John Opel called a 'company within a company') with a 12-man development team located in Florida. Its independence from IBM's traditions had an important impact on the design, production, and marketing of the PC.

The most significant breaks with IBM tradition were the widespread purchase of components and the open architecture of the PC. The core of the new microcomputer was the Intel 8088 chip, the first 16-bit microprocessor used in a microcomputer.[12]

The new operating system that was required to match the PC's hardware capabilities, called PC/DOS, was developed under contract by Microsoft. By the terms of the contract, Microsoft kept the copyright to PC/DOS and thus the right to sell it (or variants of it) to other microcomputer makers. Other examples of purchased components include the electronic circuit boards (from SCI Systems, Inc.), the disk drive (from Tandom Corporation), and the printer (from Epson). At one point, 75 per cent of the PC's value came from components manufactured in the Far East.

Like the Apple II, the PC had open architecture. IBM released technical information on the PC and designed empty slots in its cabinet for additional circuit boards. This physical openness would, it was hoped, spawn production of such complementary products as monitors, printers, disk drives, memory expansion boards, and modems to facilitate communications. Only one element of the PC, the *Read-Only Memory Basic Input/Output System* (ROM BIOS), was proprietary to IBM.

The PC was introduced (with a base price of $1565) with only three applications programs available for its PC/DOS operating system— VisiCalc, BASIC, and Easywriter (a word processing program). All were written by independent firms. Although PC/DOS was modelled after CP/M (and the 8088 chip was developed from the 8085), it could not run the programs written for CP/M. Software like Wordstar and dBase II, which were written originally for CP/M, had to be modified to run on PC/DOS. It was not until later that a version of CP/M, called CP/M-86, was released that could run the older software directly on a PC. Even then, software with its origins in CP/M could not exploit the power the PC offered.

The earliest buyers of the PC were gambling that the model would be sufficiently successful that independent software firms would write the necessary new programs. The gamble paid off, and the launch of the PC was a spectacular success, especially with the business market. Within a few months, the PC had gained 6 per cent of the total market—a share that grew to exceed 30 per cent by 1984 (when Apple took 11 per cent). PC production increased from about 20 000 units in 1981 to 225 000 in 1982 and to more than 420 000 in 1983 (when its market share exceeded Apple's for the first time). IBM's microcomputer hardware sales in 1984 were over $2500 million. Market shares by installations are shown in Table 2.1.

The success of the PC and its open architecture gave birth to whole

Table 2.1   Market leadership and market shares (%)

1978		1981		1984		1987	
Tandy	(50)	Apple	(20)	IBM	(33)	IBM	(26)
Comm.	(12)	Tandy	(15)	Apple	(11)	Apple	(8)
Apple	(10)	H-P	(12)	Comm.	(6)	Compaq	(5)
		Comm.	(7)	Tandy	(4)	Olivetti	(4)

Source: Grindley, P. and R. McBryde, Standards strategy for personal computers. In Berg, J. and H. Schummy (eds)., *An Analysis of the Information Technology Standardization Process*, North Holland, Amsterdam, 1990.

industries of IBM-compatible complementary products. Applications software was the biggest. Although IBM itself was the largest publisher of microcomputer software in 1984 with over 100 titles, most were not written by IBM and were equally available from their creators. In some instances, IBM sold the software with its own logo on the box, in other cases (especially with extremely popular programs like Lotus 1-2-3), IBM only acted as a distributor.

The whole microsoftware industry comprised around 5000 firms by 1983. In 1984, there were 11 000 different programs available for the PC, and industry sales amounted to $3300 million. Much of the increase in PC software came at the expense of Apple. Software written for Apple constituted about 85 per cent of the microcomputer software market in 1982. It fell to 35 per cent in 1983.

The implication of the growth of the PC-compatible software, peripheral hardware, and service industries was that various characteristics of the PC that were important for compatibility became *de facto* industry standards. Any independent producer with a hardware or software product that relied on linkage to a microcomputer almost automatically developed it to the 'PC standard'. Similarly, as we will see in the next section, most *other* microcomputer producers designed their machines to be compatible with the PC standard so that their customers could have access to the huge installed base of PC-complementary products.

To the extent that the PC defined a *de facto* industry standard, that standard was imprecise. At the broadest level, it included not only the MS/DOS operating system (the generic name for PC/DOS) and Intel's 8088 chip, but also the keyboard layout,[13] 360K floppy disk storage,[14] various physical interconnections, and 64K of random access memory.

In general, subsequent versions of the PC were compatible with earlier versions in the sense that complements to the evolving PC models (e.g. the PC/XT introduced in 1983 and PC/AT in 1984) could operate on earlier models and vice versa. Enhanced releases of MS/ DOS were designed to maintain upward compatibility. And newer Intel microprocessors (e.g. the 8088, 8088-2, 8086, 80186, and 80286) were designed to be compatible as well.

Compatibility within the PC family was not always possible, however. Problems arose, for example, with a low cost model, the PC Jr, whose memory was too small to run many 'standard' applications; with the IBM portable, which used 3.5-inch diskettes; and with the PC/AT, which used high density 5.25-inch diskettes. Furthermore, compatibility within the various versions of the PC—and with other microcomputers—was often achieved by the expedient of gateway technologies. For example, a recent version of Word Perfect required the user to identify the attached printer from a menu of 209 different printer models. And to set communications protocols, users were often required to specify a variety of technical characteristics of their hardware.

The clones of the PC

The PC caused the bankruptcy of many of the firms selling only the now-obsolete 8-bit machines. But it also afforded an obvious counter-strategy for smaller microcomputer makers and potential entrants—the manufacture of PC-like machines that would prove compatible with the PC's stock of complementary products. Survivors of the CP/M era that converted to making PC-compatibles included Zenith, Leading Edge, and Kaypro.

Since so many of the PC's components, both hardware and software, were available from independent suppliers, there were few barriers to would-be makers of a PC 'clone'. Only IBM's proprietary ROM BIOS chip stood in the way. The first firm to sell a clone—within a year of the introduction of the PC—was Compaq. Compaq's in-house research and development department followed a process of 'reverse engineering' to duplicate the ROM BIOS chip's functions without infringing on the IBM copyright. Compaq's products used the same microprocessors and operating system as did the PC. Compaq solved the inevitable problem that all the clones faced—the need to differentiate its micro from the PC—by offering portability (sometimes called 'lugability' since the machine weighed 28 lb (13 kg)), high quality, and better technology (within the constraints of the PC standard) at prices comparable to those of the PC. Started in 1982, Compaq set a US growth record with $111

25

million in sales in 1983 when it went public. In 1987, the company's revenues exceeded $1000 million.

The clone makers only assembled purchased components, and most relied on three companies to supply critical electronic technology. Phoenix Technologies, like Compaq, managed to duplicated IBM's proprietary ROM BIOS technology without violating the copyright. Chips & Technologies introduced five chips that performed the functions of a 63-chip set used in the PC/AT. These five chips were used in 85 per cent of all clones sold. Western Digital Corporation was the third principal firm to make clone components.

For the first few years of the PC's life, IBM was able to earn a price premium on its 'original'. The premium has been estimated at $1570 per unit in 1985.[15] But as the clones established a reputation for perfect compatibility, the premium attached to the IBM brand name diminished. Price competition intensified, IBM's profit margins declined continually, and in the 1983 slump in the market, a number of producers including Osborne, Texas Instruments, and Computer Devices left the industry or went bankrupt.

In the increasingly competitive industry, IBM progressively lost ground to the clones. In 1986 alone, IBM lost 20 per cent of its market share to the approximately 350 PC clone makers world-wide. Sales of clones passed those of IBM's PC in 1986, and in 1987, about 4.5 million clones were sold compared to only 1.6 million PCs.

Apple computers

Apple's follow-up to its extremely successful Apple II family was the Apple III, introduced in 1980. The Apple III had three times the memory of the Apple II and was intended for the business market where it would not cannibalize sales of the Apple II, concentrated as they were in the home and education markets. But like the Apple II, the Apple III was an 8-bit machine, and thus its improvement in speed and power was modest. Priced at about $4500, it was very expensive. Furthermore, it used a different operating system, which achieved compatibility with the Apple II in such a cumbersome way that independent software firms were dissuaded from writing programs for it.

Technologically dated, plagued with design bugs and production problems, and poorly supported with software, the Apple III was a flop. In 1983, sales averaged 3500 units monthly (compared to 30 000 Apple II units monthly). Apple could look back on 5 years of 150 per cent average annual growth, but it was still a one-product company with 97 per cent of its sales revenue coming from the Apple II family. Furthermore, its impressive historical growth was fundamentally threatened by the PC, which was a disaster for Apple. From 1980 to 1983, Apple saw its microcomputer market share fall from 37 per cent to 19 per cent.

In 1983, Apple introduced the Lisa. Unlike the Apple III, Lisa was no lemon. It was technologically sophisticated (driven by the 32-bit Motorola 68000 chip) and 'user-friendly' with excellent graphic capabilities, 'windows' offering split screen viewing, icon-based commands, and a 'mouse' to move the cursor. Bundled in its internal memory were six applications programs (including word processing and financial software). But with a price of nearly $10 000, it was out of the reach of the household market (and of much of the corporate market to which it was directed). Its graphics were so complex that despite its 32-bit chip, it ran slower than a PC. Worse yet, it was incompatible with all previous Apples and with the now-standard PC. Apple had chosen to limit market access to the Lisa's technology so that independent firms could not encroach on the machine's potential revenue. Of course, the result was that Apple bore the full cost of all aspects of the Lisa's development including the applications software—a task that required three years and $50 million to complete.

High priced and poorly supported with software, the Lisa, like the Apple III, was a failure. Only 20 000 machines were shipped in 1983, that is, half the forecast. An additional blow to the Lisa was the introduction of the now-famous Lotus 1-2-3 spreadsheet program for MS/DOS systems which was clearly superior to VisiCalc in the business market.

The Lisa was re-released in 1984 in three newer versions with lower prices. Simultaneously, a less expensive (at about $2500), less powerful micro was introduced—the Macintosh. The Mac development program had run parallel to but independently from (and to a considerable extent in competition with) that of the Lisa. Both programs had been started in 1979. Both were targeted at the business market. Both used the same 32-bit microprocessor. Nevertheless, they were very different machines. The Mac used a rigid 3.5-inch diskette (a Sony design) rather than the existing standard 5.25-inch floppy diskette. And the Mac's operating system was totally different from that of the Lisa so that Macs could not run Lisa software (although one of the new Lisa models was able to run Macintosh software).

The Mac's architecture was closed to outside firms, and users were warned that their warranties would be void if their machines' cases were opened. In an effort to mitigate the applications software problem that hurt the Lisa, Apple contracted with 100 software companies to develop programs for the Mac. Yet Apple was late in publishing the software tools necessary for the third-party programmers, and the Mac's small internal memory was another discouragement to them. Regardless of these problems, most software firms were dedicated to PC applications anyway. So there was almost no third-party Mac software available at the time of its introduction.

Early sales of the Mac were good overall (the Mac had a record debut for a micro with 275 000 units sold in the first year), but they were disappointing in the business segment. The machine's acceptance was limited by the dearth of software, its lack of a hard disk,[16] and by its small core memory. By 1984, IBM's share of the business market reached 40 per cent (from 18 per cent only two years earlier), while Apple's share fell from to 11 per cent (from 22 per cent two years earlier). At the end of 1984, the Mac was in serious trouble.

In 1985, the strategy for the Mac was fundamentally revised to one of greater openness. Any and all software and hardware peripheral makers were encouraged to develop products for it. And for the first time, an expansion port was included in the machine to permit networking and data communications.

The Macintosh's sales record quickly began to improve, and by early 1987, Apple had shipped 1 million units. More than 3000 programs for it were available on the market, and about 100 firms were making software or peripheral products. Especially important was Microsoft's release of Excel, a powerful spreadsheet designed for the Mac.

In May 1987 (just a month before IBM introduced its PS/2), Apple released two new Macs. The Mac SE was roughly similar to the earlier Mac, but it came with a hard disk. The Mac II, on the other hand, used a more powerful microprocessor, the Motorola 68020. Both new products were compatible with earlier versions of the Mac. The SE could be altered to accept PC-compatible software and could share files with PC's and IBM mainframes using readily available gateways. The Mac II, while using its own proprietary operating system, was fully compatible with the PC and even with the venerable Apple II.

Apple has recently initiated a strategy of increased compatibility with other firms' products. In early 1988, Apple and DEC announced a joint technology alliance to develop compatibility (in particular, data interchange) between their respective product lines. The alliance was widely considered natural since DEC was strong in minicomputers and in computing power in general, while Apple's strength, confined to micros, was in graphics and user-friendliness. One tactic was to encourage third-party investment in the task, and at a 1988 exposition, more than 30 software and hardware firms showed products to integrate Macintosh and DEC systems in a networking environment. (Third-party firms had accomplished the task previously, but the imprimatur of Apple and DEC was important to its commercial exploitation. It indicated to users the firms' commitment to maintain this compatibility rather than to sever it, perhaps unintentionally, in new products.)

In early 1988, Apple became the first microcomputer maker to offer UNIX as an operating system (as an option to the standard Apple system with the Mac II). UNIX was developed by AT & T in the 1960s, and it afforded the Mac the ability to run several programs simultaneously (called 'multi-tasking'), it accommodated multiple users simultaneously, and it was particularly adept at 'interoperability', that is, the ability to tap into programs running on other computers in a network. Since UNIX had been around for many years, programs using it existed for technical workstations, minicomputers, and even mainframes. The hope was that the Mac II with UNIX would prove ideal in an office networking environment linked via electronic mail or data exchange to larger computers made by other firms. In fact, the Mac II with UNIX broke the traditional distinction in power and price that separated the microcomputer market from the technical workstation market. (UNIX and technical workstations are discussed in detail in Chapter 5.)

To encourage more software production, Apple set up a subsidiary named Claris to develop and market software. Popular applications programs formerly sold under the Apple label, like MacPaint and MacDraw, were given to Claris. Apple only maintained ownership of its operating system. Furthermore, Claris undertook to market under the Claris label software developed by small firms that themselves lacked marketing power. The purpose of the move was to put the independent firms writing software for Macs on a more even footing with Apple's in-house programming.

Despite its dramatic changes in strategy, Apple is still a relatively small firm in the microcomputer industry with a 12.5 per cent share of the market in 1989.

Other 'non-standard' micros

Apple was not the only microcomputer maker to introduce new machines that were incompatible with the PC. In mid-1982, Digital Equipment Corporation entered the market with the Rainbow 100. The Rainbow was originally conceived as a CP/M machine, but by the time it was introduced, it had been redesigned with both the 8-bit Zilog Z-80 and the 16-bit Intel 8088 microprocessors so that it could run both CP/M and the new MS/DOS operating systems. Surprisingly, however, the Rainbow was incompatible with the IBM PC despite having the same microprocessor and essentially the same operating system. Consequently, applications programs for the Rainbow (like Multiplan, Lotus 1-2-3, and dBase II) had to be transcribed from those originally written for the PC.

Although its relative lack of software was probably enough to doom it, the Rainbow had other problems as well including late market entry, poor distribution, and a high price.

After poor sales in 1983, DEC decided to change its strategy for the Rainbow. In early 1984, it abandoned the general-purpose retail market and focused on selected vertical segments like science, engineering, and advanced graphics. However, sales remained poor in 1984 when only 101 000 units were shipped, and the Rainbow 100 was dropped in early 1985. Its replacement was the Rainbow 190 which, unlike the original 100, was compatible with DEC's line of VAX minicomputers, its word processing system, and networking programs like DECNet. At the same time, software was introduced to make existing Rainbow 100s equally compatible with the other elements of DEC's office systems. But the Rainbow 190, like the 100, was incompatible with the PC, and in 1985, DEC sold only 42 000 Rainbows.

Although DEC finally ceased Rainbow production in 1987, enough machines were in place by then to support independent firms' development of add-on products to afford some degree of IBM compatibility for the Rainbow. Eventually, Rainbow owners would have access to much (but not all) of the PC's repertoire of applications software.

The successor to the Rainbow line was the VAXmate, introduced in 1986. The VAXmate was compatible with DEC's VAX minicomputers and it was compatible with IBM's PC/AT.

Hewlett-Packard was another firm that tried to compete directly with IBM with an incompatible micro. In late 1983, it introduced the Model 150, the company's first entry into the microcomputer market. The Model 150 used the Intel 8088 chip and the MS/DOS operating system as did the PC (and the Rainbow). But the Model 150 was designed so that commands were given to it by touching images on the screen. The cost of this novelty, however, was that the machine could not be made compatible with the library of PC software. Hewlett-Packard contracted with software firms to transcribe popular PC applications for the Model 150, and some 30 firms did so, rewriting programs like WordStar and VisiCalc for touch control. Nevertheless, the Model 150, although more clearly differentiated from the PC than was the Rainbow, could not succeed in competition with the well-established PC standard, and it was abandoned.

The 'clone killers'

In April 1987, IBM unveiled its new *Personal System/2* (PS/2) product line. The new line, with a top-end model that used Intel's 32-bit 80386 microprocessor, represented a significant increase in power and speed over the PC and its clones.

The new IBM microcomputer was designed with proprietary interface standards and with customized logic chips that would make cloning difficult, and the company publicly and repeatedly announced that it would take legal action to protect its patents and copyrights. Components like disk drives that had been purchased for the PC were made in-house for the PS/2. Independent software firms were encouraged to write applications programs for the machine, but with respect to hardware, only specifications for add-on boards were released for third-party manufacture. Thus, the PS/2, widely called the 'clone killer' by the press, signalled a fundamental shift in IBM strategy to more restricted proprietary control of its microcomputer product line.

The PS/2 met with immediate problems in the market. The first was that in some significant ways it was incompatible with the PC. The PS/2 used 3.5-inch rather than 5.25-inch floppy diskettes which made its input medium incompatible (although it was possible to transcribe files from one diskette to another). And the new proprietary data bus[17]—called Micro Channel—made it impossible for the PS/2 to use the PC's add-on devices like memory extension boards. Micro Channel was particularly important to IBM because it was both a major reason for the PS/2's technological advancement over the PC and a key element of IBM's proprietary control of the machine.

The second problem with the PS/2's introduction was caused by the operating system, called OS/2, which was under joint development by IBM and Microsoft. OS/2 would offer multi-tasking and multi-user

31

capability (like UNIX) and thus would represent a major advance over MS/DOS. Furthermore, it would run all existing PC programs ensuring software compatibility with the millions of PCs and clones in use. The problem with OS/2 was that it was not available when the PS/2 was introduced. Fortunately, the PS/2 could run with MS/DOS, but this failed to utilize the full capabilities of the new computer. The first version of OS/2 would not become available until December 1987, and then only for the mid-range PS/2 models using the old 16-bit 80286 microprocessor. The version of OS/2 dedicated to the more powerful 80386 chip would not be ready until 1989.

A third though more modest problem was with the PS/2's user interface, called Presentation Manager. The user interface would allow IBM users to work in a symbol-based environment like that which Apple microcomputers afforded. But it too was unavailable and would only appear in October 1988.

To accelerate the market's conversion from the PC to the PS/2, IBM ceased production of its last PC models, the XT and AT. However, the result was to stimulate the sales of PC clone makers like Compaq and competitors like Apple in the latter half of 1987. In the three months following the introduction of the PS/2, Compaq's sales rose 82 per cent and its profits more than tripled.

How effectively the PS/2 could kill clones depended initially on the size of two obstacles it created for would-be clone makers. The first obstacle was their access to OS/2 (and to a lesser extent, to Presentation Manager). But, in an apparent surprise to IBM, Microsoft, which jointly owned the rights to both, publicly announced that it would license them to other hardware makers.

The other obstacle was IBM's proprietary hardware, but many of the same firms that cloned the PC (e.g. Phoenix Technologies, Chips & Technologies, and Western Digital Corporation) managed to produce chips that emulated proprietary PS/2 technology. Clones entered the market (although none circumvented Micro Channel) with no legal challenge. As this happened, however, the wisdom of cloning began to be questioned.

The revolt of the clones

Paradoxically, just as IBM's effort to prevent cloning of the PS/2 began to look like a failure, it also began to look too successful. By threatening the existence of an industry of firms born and raised by cloning the PC, IBM provoked its revolt and may have fundamentally undermined the entire PS/2 product line. The revolt of what the trade press has called the 'Gang of Nine' came in the autumn of 1988. The revolutionaries included Compaq (the leader), Hewlett-Packard, Olivetti, Tandy, NEC, Epson, AST Research, Wyse Technologies, and Zenith Data Systems. Although no single member was as large as IBM, the Gang collectively had 50 per cent more than IBM's microcomputer market share. And the nine official members of the Gang were joined in spirit by Intel, Microsoft, and more than 80 other companies.

The objective of the Gang of Nine was to develop an alternative to Micro Channel—the central component of IBM's proprietary PS/2 technology. The alternative was a 32-bit data bus called the *Extended Industry Standard Architecture* (EISA) which was to be introduced in late 1989. EISA, like Micro Channel, would raise computer operating speeds, and in technological terms, the two systems had essentially equivalent capabilities. But ironically, EISA was compatible with IBM PC add-on boards whereas IBM's Micro Channel was not. Thus, with EISA, computer users could upgrade from their PC or PC-compatible micros without scrapping much of their existing investment.[18]

One spur to the revolutionaries was the poor start of PS/2, Micro Channel, and OS/2. In mid-1987, the PS/2 had only about 15 per cent of the US market. Prospective customers appeared concerned about Micro Channel's potential to secure IBM's monopoly control of the post-PC standard. More importantly, however, OS/2 continued to create problems. It proved to require massive memory capacity and thus was expensive and unattractive to the large proportion of users uninterested in multi-tasking and multi-user capability. And it had serious bugs. So IBM salespeople were encouraging customers to get a PS/2 with MS/DOS rather than OS/2.

A final possible drag on OS/2 was the possibility that it would be eclipsed by UNIX and eventually orphaned. OS/2 had no functionality that UNIX did not also have, and UNIX had a large portfolio of applications (although few were suited to the typical microcomputer user). Microsoft, the co-developer of OS/2, was simultaneously the leading supplier of UNIX (more precisely, of XENIX, Microsoft's proprietary version of UNIX). So Microsoft had a potential conflict of interset in OS/2. IBM was already providing its version of UNIX (UNIX AIX) in its top-of-the-line PS/2s, and there was growing interest on the part of other micro producers to offer UNIX-based machines. In particular, AT & T, Sun Microsystems, and Xerox were cooperating on a UNIX-based machine with a new graphical user interface called 'Open

Look' that offered performance like that of Apple machines. This would be direct competition for the PS/2, OS/2, and Presentation Manager.

The morass that the PS/2 found itself in provoked the Gang to reject the strategy of cloning the PS/2 (and risking an IBM lawsuit) and to opt instead to develop a new hardware standard around its proposed EISA data bus. With its own hardware, the Gang would then be able to follow whatever developments occurred in operating systems. Its first EISA chip was demonstrated in 1989, at which time 20 companies were designing compatible machines.

The initiative of the Gang of Nine to wrest control of the PS/2 standard from IBM had a number of consequences. One was market confusion. Potential customers were now required to choose between: (a) PS/2 and Micro Channel, which implied scrapping PC-compatible add-on boards and facing the risk of IBM's monopoly; (b) the mid-range PS/2 model that was offered without Micro Channel and whose 16-bit chip offered little improvement in capability over a late-vintage PC clone; (c) waiting until late 1989 for EISA; or (d) a clone of the PS/2 with or without a Micro Channel equivalent. A final alternative—the worst for the entire group of firms—was to buy a Mac.

The exact form of IBM's counterattack is unclear at this time. A rumoured possibility was a version of the standard 32-bit PS/2 without Micro Channel. The drawback was that it would acknowledge the defeat of the Micro Channel technology, and such an acknowledgement would have two unattractive consequences. It would provoke customers to question the merits of the entire PS/2 line since Micro Channel was one of the principal justifications for upgrading from the PC. Secondly, Micro Channel was the technological and symbolic arena where IBM would kill the clones. Without it, the entire PS/2 would lie as open as the PC had been.

A second strategy, which IBM announced in April 1988, was to license PS/2 and Micro Channel technology to *encourage* cloning. Tandy and Olivetti were among the first to produce Micro Channel machines. Compaq acquired the right to Micro Channel technology as well although the company has not shown interest in using it.[19] Simultaneously, IBM announced that it would raise licence fees for the technology, in some instances by as much as 500 per cent (when multiple patents were involved). However, later in 1988, IBM stated that it would negotiate easier terms for firms interested in licensing its technology.

At this point of the story, there are few clones of the PS/2—but not for the reason that IBM had hoped—and little market interest in the ones that are available.

B   ANALYSIS

When one analyses a case, one must be aware that what might appear to be the result of conscious corporate strategy was in fact either the unexpected consequence of actions taken for other reasons or the result of pure circumstances in the absence of any conscious strategy at all. And even if the characters in the case were to attest to their successful strategy formulation and execution, that attestation could be nothing more than the normal inclination all of us have for *ex post* rationalization. To the extent that this occurs, this case and its analysis err in attributing strategic intent to observed behaviour. This is a risk in analysing any case, but it is particularly pronounced here because some company employees believe that neither Apple nor IBM (in the early 1980s) had any clearly defined product strategy at all.

Nevertheless, there is a rationale for attributing intent to observed outcome despite the risk. For one thing, behaviour can be rational in the sense of having and pursuing an objective even though neither the objective nor the means to it is ever articulated—nor even conscious. For example, Apple employees may complain that the company under Steve Jobs's leadership had no direction and that it would be mistaken to say that the Apple II's open and the Mac's closed architectures were anything but accidental. Yet it is also possible that the vision was there and was a significant determinant of results even though it was obscured by the chaos of Jobs's leadership style.

A second rationale is that for didactic purposes, it is useful to *assume* that it is strategy that dictates results. To do otherwise would obviate the opportunity to analyse the relationship between the alternatives that were available to decision makers and the logic for and against each. In any case, we will often infer strategic purpose from actions, conscious that in some instances, strategy may not have been articulated or even conscious to those to whom it is attributed, and that in some instances there may truly have been no strategy at all.

The industry from 1975 to 1981
Prior to the introduction of the Tandy, Commodore, and Apple machines in 1976 and 1977, there were no significant standards in the

industry. This period of market creation corresponds to the early periods in the automobile and videotape recorder industries discussed in subsequent chapters when the products were experimental and when any effort at standardization would have been technologically and commercially premature.

But significant changes began to overtake the industry with the introduction of the computers of the late 1970s. For the first time, one sees complete systems appearing with components that originate in different industries and that require standards for coordination on the supply side. And as more expertise is embodied in the product and less required of the user, a dynamic process is started on the demand side in which the potential market expands rapidly and networks of users begin to appear with an interest in sharing complementary products (in this case, the software). All of this is roughly analogous to what happened in the car industry with respect to the evolution of the technology and the development of the service infrastructure (as will be recounted later).

It is significant that the first rough standards in the microcomputer industry—in both hardware and software—originated with the industry's suppliers, Digital Research Corporation, Intel, and a few other chip makers, rather than with the microcomputer manufacturers themselves. The floppy disk represents another example of a standard that, although introduced by Apple, was not the proprietary creation of the microcomputer makers.

Taking the operating system as a case in point, since Digital Research (and later, Microsoft) did not make computers, it had no motive to restrict access to CP/M (or to MS/DOS in the case of Microsoft) beyond charging a royalty. It is worth reflecting on how this industry might have evolved had all the micro manufacturers developed their own operating systems as did Apple and Tandy. The result would presumably have been an industry cursed with incompatibility just as has been the mainframe industry and for the same reason (see Chapter 5). This leads one to surmise that *de facto* standardization is relatively more likely in an industry that is not vertically integrated. It is not a coincidence that in this industry, microprocessors, which are universally purchased, have always been more standardized than operating systems in which there is some vertical integration. This supposition is consistent with the hypothesis that standards are most likely to be voluntarily accepted when they are competitively neutral. Since technological standards that originate with the suppliers would normally be so (unless there were some form of discrimination), it is often the task of suppliers to set standards (either willingly or under pressure from their customers).[20]

The three different strategies of the earliest major producers illustrate the basic alternatives that appear repeatedly throughout the story of microcomputers. One, used by firms like Osborne that made CP/M machines, was to purchase a standard operating system (and microprocessor) and thereby to join an existing network of users. This strategy would appeal most to producers with limited financial resources and little or no software expertise. It gives them immediate access to applications software, albeit at the opportunity cost of lost software income. But it also makes it difficult for a producer to differentiate its product from others that share the standard operating system. (This problem was especially acute among the hundreds of firms that cloned the PC in the early to mid-1980s).

The second strategy—Apple's with the Apple II—was to develop a proprietary operating system, but to reveal its details and to open the architecture of the hardware so that independent firms could produce complementary products. The attraction of this strategy is that it affords the firm the opportunity to differentiate its product line technologically (since to the user, a microcomputer's characteristics are fundamentally determined by the operating system), and it earns the firm the rents that accrue from the hardware and the operating system.

The major drawback is that it is impossible to lock customers into the firm's proprietary technology and then to exploit the lock-in through high margin sales of complementary products. With Apple's strategy, the market for complementary products is surrendered to other firms. The only possible lock-in is via the sale of subsequent generations of hardware—assuming that upward compatibility is guaranteed. (As we saw, this is something that Apple repeatedly failed to do.)

Apple's strategy was clearly very successful in the first generation of the industry for the following reasons. First, there was no truly dominant 'open' system standard at the time (i.e. a system that could be purchased on the open market) so that the disadvantage to the consumer of buying into Apple's proprietary world was not easily avoided. And in any case, being tied to an Apple entailed little risk of exploitation for the reasons noted above. Second, Apple had an excellent product and a few applications that were very popular. Third, these applications, although not numerous, were sufficient to start the momentum that led to more with the result that the Apple soon had the largest network of software of any model. (And fortunately for the Apple II users, Apple continually upgraded its hardware.)

The third strategy—Tandy's—was to restrict independent firms' access to its proprietary operating system and to its micro's hardware architecture. And here we can see—at the earliest stage of the industry's history—the fundamental conflict that all the firms faced between two common objectives: setting a standard and profiting from it. A strategy of restricting access to technology might well preserve for a company the full monopoly rent for both hardware and software. But at the same time, it dramatically reduced the likelihood that the technology would command any reasonable market share. In fact, Tandy's policy of extreme restrictiveness eventually proved untenable in the face of more open alternatives. The same was true of Apple's very restrictive policy with the Lisa and the early Mac. One might surmise that the only circumstances in which complete restriction would prove possible is when all firms pursued this same policy. Again, this is analogous to the situation that prevailed for a long time in mainframe computers and is only now beginning to break down in the face of the open standards movement as Chapter 5 describes.

The *de facto* standardization of the PC

The brief overview of the basic microcomputer strategies in the previous section prompts an obvious question that we will try to answer here. Why did IBM, a firm with enormous financial resources, with software (and even microprocessor) production capabilities, and with a corporate history of proprietary technology, choose such an open strategy with the PC? Was it done consciously? Was it sensible given what was known at the time and, alternatively, what was known later? And finally, what were the most important consequences for the industry?

IBM's strategic thinking for the PC was dominated by the perceived need to enter the market quickly. The leading company in the worldwide computer industry simply had to be in its fastest growing segment. The need for rapid development led to the decision to set up what was essentially a venture capital firm in Florida that was isolated from the normal internal controls of the company. Independence, isolation, and time pressure in turn resulted in the purchase of the key elements of the product—the operating system and the microprocessor—as well as less important components like the video screen, disk drive, and printer. (Another consequence, that was not particularly important at the time

38

but which became more so later, was that the PC was incompatible with other products in IBM's product line.)

Was the strategy wise given what the company knew at the time? It was in the sense that the PC was launched quickly and was an overwhelming early market success. It was so successful that in 1983, there was a widespread industry opinion (and perhaps an IBM fear) that the company was close to monopolizing the microcomputer market. *Business Week* entitled its 3 October, 1983 cover story, 'Personal computers: and the winner is IBM'.

IBM had a significant first mover advantage in the new generation of micros that persisted for a number of years and allowed the company a price premium at least until the middle of the decade. There were a number of reasons why IBM might have felt that this initial advantage would be all that would ever be needed for the PC. Little of the PC was proprietary, but what was (the ROM BIOS) should have protected the machine from quick and massive copying. And the market would suspect that the early clones would be imperfectly compatible—as, indeed, they were. Finally, IBM never anticipated a sales record even of the same order of magnitude as that which developed for the PC. (Indeed, the entire computer industry from its very beginnings in the 1940s has a history of seriously underestimating demand.) In any case, since IBM expected a small market, it was reasonable for them to believe that a strong initial position with the safeguards noted above might carry the PC through most of its lifetime.

Yet with hindsight, one can fault IBM. Although it took a risk introducing a product—and a new standard—with few complementary products, the 16-bit machine was a major technological leap that would make obsolete much of the installed base of 8-bit software in the household market, and that would create a standard in the vacuum of the business office where microcomputers were still alien. This is precisely the circumstance when it is easiest to set a standard. And IBM had an obvious motive to succeed, the resources to do so, and such an enormous corporate reputation—in particular for preserving its customers' investments—that consumers and independent firms were confident that the product would succeed. Their confidence was self-justifying, and IBM's failure to share it must be regarded in retrospect as a fundamental error.

Other errors followed this one. Had IBM correctly forecast the market, it might not have made the PC so vulnerable to eventual cloning. How could this have been done? First, IBM might not have

39

agreed to Microsoft's demand for the right to license the operating system. In the limit, it might have developed its own operating system, which it had the capability to do. Other investments that might have increased the proprietary content of the PC and thus raised entry barriers were surely possible as well, and their expected returns would increase with the market forecast.

This reasoning assumes that the PC would have set the industry 16-bit standard even with a proprietary operating system. This assumption contradicts the hypothesis stated above that *de facto* standards are most easily set outside the industry (i.e. the hypothesis that it would be much easier for Microsoft to set an operating system standard than for IBM to do so). Yet there is at least some reason to believe that IBM might have proven an exception, just as was Apple with the Apple II. For one thing, the PC entered a market segment—the business segment—where there was no other competing standard. Its early success was so complete that it had essentially set the standard well before significant cloning had ever started. In other words, *the IBM PC was the standard* at least for a couple of years before cloning shifted the standard to generic MS/DOS-based machines. Had MS/DOS (or an equivalent) been IBM's proprietary operating system, there might have been some modest reduction in the size of the market, but it is unlikely that any other system could have overtaken it. It is worth noting that the number two seller, Apple, was itself pursuing exactly this strategy, that is, a restricted proprietary operating system and active courting of independent applications software development.

If IBM had developed a proprietary operating system, it could have used its headstart there and its knowledge of the system's intricacies to develop key applications programs (like word processing or spreadsheets) that, in such a fast moving industry, might themselves have become standards even if they were technologically inferior to what would undoubtedly have appeared later from independent firms.

All these changes would have delayed the PC's introduction. It is impossible to know for how long, although two or three years is a reasonable guess. But there was no other imminent 16-bit machine threatening the nascent PC, and the rewards for retaining dominance in the microcomputer market (and the rents from the operating system and possibly from applications software) suggest that a delay might have been worth while.

Further evidence of the wisdom of a more proprietary PC is provided by IBM's 'clone killer' strategy for the PS/2. This is precisely the strategy

40

outlined above. Unfortunately, the competitive situation in the late 1980s when the PS/2 was introduced was much less amenable to the strategy's execution than was the situation in 1981. When the PS/2 appeared, others had already introduced 32-bit hardware, other operating systems already offered multi-tasking, and Apple offered a user environment that Presentation Manager could only copy. So the PS/2 would have to do more than just set a standard in a vacuum as did the PC. It would face the much more difficult task of displacing some existing standards that were functionally equivalent. Furthermore, in the late 1980s, IBM faced established firms with experience cloning IBM machines and whose continued existence was thought to hinge on repeating that experience. And it faced a customer market spoiled by its experience with the open standards of the PC era.

It is surprising that IBM was so mistaken in its PC strategy because the company lived through similar problems in the 1960s and 1970s with its mainframe Systems 360 and 370. This episode in IBM's history is recounted in some detail in the chapter on open systems (Chapter 5) and will not be repeated here. Let it suffice to say that these systems were so successful that they too prompted widespread copying, and to some extent their architecture and software became *de facto* standards. With that standardization came a number of undesirable consequences for IBM that were repeated with the PC.

What were the consequences of IBM's loss of control of the PC standard? The first was that entry barriers to the industry dropped to insignificance, and new entrants poured in. These new entrants were not component parts specialists as is often the case in other industries. (The analogy would be the entry of the plug-compatible manufacturers in the story of the System 360.) Software and hardware specialists selling complementary products had been welcomed from the beginning. Rather, the new entrants were assemblers of full microcomputer systems in direct competition with the PC.

The growing dominance of the PC standard and the entry of the clones changed the nature of competition in the industry. With the effective elimination of differentiation in operating system and microprocessor technology (Apple notwithstanding), producers had one fewer weapon with which to compete. The competitive tools that remained were price and technological differentiation (e.g. portability) within the constraints of MS/DOS and the Intel 8088. Both were tried. Compaq was probably the best example of successful technological diffentiation. The nameless clones competed purely on the basis of price. Their price competition brought the entire industry price structure down to the point where few producers made money, and IBM announced that unless margins were improved in the next generation of microcomputer, it would consider leaving the market. This admission set the stage for IBM's 'clone killer' strategy.

Another consequence of standardization concerned the amount and type of product variety that was offered by the market. In one sense, standardization reduced variety. The success of the PC caused companies that once differentiated themselves with their proprietary operating systems, like Tandy, to switch to MS/DOS. Others that tried to offer a clearly differentiated but incompatible micro, like Hewlett-Packard, failed. In the end, Apple was the only firm of any consequence that had a fundamentally different technology to that of the PC and its clones. And that statement exaggerates the situation since the Apple II family competed in a different market segment (mostly households and educational institutions). The Macintosh was the only microcomputer ever to become a successful competitor to a MS/DOS machine until the PS/2 (whose success is yet to be truly proven).

Although *de facto* standardization reduced the technological variety of microcomputer models on the market, it increased the variety of complementary products for those models. More software, more peripherals, and more 'mix and match' variations became possible. This illustrates an inevitable trade-off that standardization creates between reduced variety in the core technology that becomes standardized (microcomputer hardware and software architecture in this case) and increased variety of products complementary to that technology (e.g. applications software, add-on boards, etc.).

A final consequence was that there were significant rents from standards. But those rents, which might have been earned in the microcomputer industry, accrued instead to the industry's suppliers. In particular, they accrued to the two firms that really 'owned' the PC standard—Microsoft and Intel.

Apple's success despite itself

It is ironic that IBM chose a strategy of open architecture with the PC while Apple did the opposite with the Apple III, Lisa, and the early Mac. One would have expected their strategies to be reversed. IBM clearly had the resources and tradition appropriate to a strategy of greater self-sufficiency. Apple, by contrast, was much smaller, financially weaker, and thus less naturally prepared for a strategy of restricted technology. Futhermore, the Apple II with which Apple had pioneered a strategy of open architecture, was a tremendous success—and the company's only success. A final argument that would have supported a policy of openness at Apple was that by 1982 or 1983, the PC's repertoire of complementary products was large and growing rapidly, making the successful introduction of a closed architecture, incompatible machine especially difficult.

The explanation for Apple's misconstrued strategy of closed architecture lies in Steve Jobs's vision of the Mac—a product that was inordinately dependent on its creator's unorthodox ideas.[21] The Mac was to be the Model T of the computer industry—rugged, simple to use, cheap, reliable, and so highly standardized that it could be mass produced in a dedicated factory. This philosophy necessitated unique hardware architecture and incompatibility with the PC (which was incidentally felt to be so uninspired that it was not worth copying anyway). The logic for the closed architecture was that only by 'locking the box' could Apple guarantee its reliability and remain faithful to the simplicity of its appeal. The fact that the Mac was to be the figurative 'everyman's' computer implied an individuality for the user with which the notion of connectivity to alien machines in an office network was anathema. (Even the word 'system' had the unattractive connotation at Apple of a relationship between different kinds of equipment.)

There are a number of ironies in this story. It is ironic that IBM chose the name *Personal Computer* for its micro because Jobs's product concept was more suited to that label. The problem with Jobs's concept, of course, was that—in an ironic parallel to the experience of his idol, Henry Ford—Jobs froze his product in a single unalterable form. A frozen design of a one-model product line with a limited set of applications programs was not appropriate in a period of rapid market development and proliferating customer needs. The PC's open architecture was to Jobs what GM was to Ford. And it is ironic that the product that set the industry standard—the PC—was not really 'standardized'. It was really the Mac that was standardized in the figurative sense of being available in any colour as long as it was black.

The shift to open architecture with the Mac in 1985, and the beginning of the Mac's improved sales performance, came because Jobs was pushed aside that year by John Sculley whom Jobs had hired in 1983. Sculley perceived correctly that Apple could not survive dependent on the home and educational markets, and that to succeed in the business segment, its computers must interconnect with IBM's office products. It would be impossible, he knew, to overcome the power of IBM's installed base no matter how good the Mac was. Unable to beat that installed base, the logical strategy was to join it. Even though he provoked hostility at Apple, Sculley redesigned the Mac with more openness, started to develop IBM connectivity, and subcontracted production of many components like disk drives, file servers, and printers that had previously been made at higher cost in-house.

Sculley was even rumoured to have considered allowing another company to build a Mac-compatible machine (i.e. to use Apple's proprietary operating system). AT & T was supposedly the candidate.[22] Irrespective of whether the rumour was true or not, the Mac was never copied.

Sculley had many conflicts with Jobs, but he never contradicted Jobs's view that Apple should avoid the ranks of the IBM clones. This steadfast preference for its own proprietary operating system is the one consistent and unique element of Apple's strategy. This is a policy that is quite separate from that of closed hardware architecture, and it has been pursued without change even when the company shifted between closed and open hardware architecture. Why has Apple so consistently preferred its own proprietary operating systems, and what have the consequences been?

The explanation is that the company's culture (at least into the mid-1980s) favoured radical technological innovation over strategic market analysis and it favoured individualistic behaviour over committees. Freedom to innovate was cherished in Apple, and standards were perceived to be a constraint on that freedom. (One should note that when IBM sent its PC development team to Florida to come up with an innovative product, it came back with something that was incompatible with all other IBM products.) That Apple did not produce an IBM-compatible should not be a surprise when one considers that the company rarely produced computer models that were compatible with each other! In 1984, Apple was selling four major product lines (the Apple II, Apple III, Lisa, and Macintosh), none of which was perfectly compatible with any other, let alone with other firms' microcomputers.

Has Apple been successful with its dogged resistance to IBM compatibility? Clearly not in the few years following the release of the PC. The Apple III and the Lisa were failures. Their failures could be attributed to a variety of problems, but incompatibility with other firms' computers was clearly a major one.

And yet, the evidence of the Apple II and now the Mac shows that proprietary operating systems can succeed in this industry even at the worst of times—which the mid-1980s surely were for promulgating an alternative to the PC standard. The difference between the Apple III, Lisa, and the pre-1985 Mac on one hand, and the Apple II and recent Mac on the other, was the difference in the attitude Apple took towards third-party development of complementary hardware and software products. When the hardware architecture was open and when independent software firms were encouraged to write applications, proprietary operating systems proved feasible

It is remarkable, and a major tribute to Apple, that it has managed to survive and profit with restricted proprietary operating system standards that were incompatible with the open standards (first CP/M and then MS/DOS) that otherwise swept the industry. The economic forces in the microcomputer industry pushing a convergence to one standard were very strong, at least in the beginning. (They can be compared to those discussed in the case of VCRs in this book.) How was Apple able to sustain a very small network in the face of the network economies that favoured the PC and its compatibles?

The answer is that the Mac was sufficiently well differentiated from the PC. Its level of technology (its 32-bit microprocessor) was a generation ahead of the PC's and afforded it the power to generate high quality graphics and to be 'user-friendly'. It was particularly well suited to desk-top publishing, and that application gave it a beach-head from which to grow. This differentiation would have been technologically impossible had Apple chosen to build its hardware around the PC's standards.

Another factor favourable to the Mac was that the microcomputer market had grown to be so large that the network economies of a single standard were at least partially exhausted. In early 1988, for example, there were about 90 different database management programs available for MS/DOS. With so much MS/DOS software crowding the market, new Mac applications (like Microsoft's Excel spreadsheet) and transcriptions of popular MS/DOS software (like Microsoft's transcription of Word) were potentially very profitable for independent software firms. Apple's operating system was not the industry-wide standard, but Microsoft, as an example, was successful with Excel and many other products it developed for Apple. About 15 per cent of the company's revenues come from applications for Apple computers.

Apple has not only survived in an industry dominated by a different and incompatible standard but also it has prospered. Its product distinctiveness has allowed it to price high enough to earn the margins (reportedly exceeding 50 per cent on the Mac) necessary to support the research and development needed for the strategy. The company was profitable throughout the period of the PC's ascendance. In 1983, Apple's profit as a percentage of equity was over 20 per cent. It fell to around 11 per cent in 1985 but then rebounded to 26 per cent in 1987.

Apple's failure to set the industry's standards, if that were ever an objective, may have left the firm in a small pond, but it is a big fish—a monopolist—in it. IBM won the inter-standards competition, but it was a Pyrrhic victory because it lost the intra-standard battle.

Now that all the microcomputer firms are following it into the third generation, Apple faces some new challenges.[23] One is that OS/2 and Presentation Manager can duplicate the Mac's visual features, so that the Mac is no longer distinctive in this respect. And virtually every firm that writes software for the Mac (e.g. Microsoft) is transcribing versions for the PS/2. So Apple must re-create a basis for differentiation. Claris is intended to help by improving the rewards for independent Mac software production. At this point, however, Claris is struggling, and in mid-1988, most of its revenues were still coming from Apple II software.

Another challenge to Apple is to ensure that its microcomputers are compatible with other manufacturers' office systems—just when it must redefine its products' distinctiveness. In mid-1988, Apple had only 6 per cent of the corporate market by installations (compared with IBM's 54 per cent and Compaq's 9 per cent). The joint technology alliance with DEC, which was announced in early 1988, was intended to address the challenge as are the continuing investments to enable the Mac to run PC and PS/2 programs and to integrate the Mac into the IBM office environment.

The dropout of the incompatibles

DEC, like Apple, tried to sell a non-PC-compatible microcomputer in direct competition with the PC. Unlike Apple, DEC failed. One explanation for the failure is that whereas the Mac was technologically differentiated from and superior to the PC, the Rainbow was not. Ironically, its minor technical differences with the PC were too great to allow compatibility and access to the PC's software and yet too small to afford any basis for compensatory differentiation. Basically, it was a PC without applications software. To the extent that there was a technological difference, the Rainbow was generally felt to be superior to the PC. The keyboard in particular was regarded as much superior.

There is again an irony in this, however, because the few comparative strengths of the Rainbow did not require it to be incompatible with the PC. Because the Rainbow ran on MS/DOS but was none the less incompatible with applications software written for the PC, its library of software was developed by adapting PC programs specifically for the Rainbow. Consequently, the Rainbow never had as much software as did the PC, nor did it have applications that were unavailable for the PC. The only competitive advantage that the Rainbow might have been imagined to have was compatibility with DEC's minicomputers. But here it was competing with DEC's line of terminals, which were more cost effective. With no advantage over the PC and a big disadvantage, it is little surprise that it failed. DEC might have sustained the Rainbow's life had it introduced conversion packages to afford it some IBM compatibility, as did independent firms, but this would have been nothing more than a palliative to Rainbow owners. It would never have helped sell more Rainbows.

The 'clone killer'?

IBM's strategy with the PS/2 was a sharp reversal from that with the PC and a tacit acknowledgement that there was no point in setting a standard unless one can profit from it. With the PS/2, IBM tried to provide enough openness so that it would define the third generation standard, yet enough proprietary technology (and a sufficiently threatening attitude towards anyone infringing on or possibly even circumventing it) so that the company could earn a profit from the standard. This strategy is what was discussed in the analysis of the PC earlier in this chapter, and it is similar to what Apple had done. There are, however, some important differences.

One peculiarity of IBM's approach with the PS/2 was that the operating system was not the key proprietary technology. Microsoft, its co-developer, had rights to it as well, and having spent $50 million developing OS/2, it should have been expected to license it to other micro producers unless forbidden to do so in its development agreement with IBM. Rather, it was Micro Channel that was the key to proprietary protection of the PS/2, and as hindsight has shown, Micro Channel did not offer protection as secure as a proprietary operating system would have done, both because it was easier to reproduce legally and because it was not entirely necessary to the computer. (In fact, the low-end PS/2 models did not have Micro Channel.)

Another important difference was that with the PS/2, IBM tried to set a new standard without radically improved functionality. Apple already had a 32-bit machine with the Mac, and Compaq as well had introduced 32-bit technology with the Intel 80386 chip. In fact, much of the improved speed that the PS/2 offered was available with PC-compatible hardware upgrades. Only Micro Channel was a significant hardware improvement, and it was most important for communications on which most users placed little value. In those markets where networking was very important, technical workstations were available.

OS/2's multi-user and multi-tasking capability was not new either (or of much value to the typical user). UNIX could do the same things, and OS/2 faced growing competition from technical workstations running UNIX in markets such as departmental systems where networks of users were important. Finally, Presentation Manager's graphic user interface brough IBM up to where Apple was with the Mac, but it did not take IBM further.[24]

So the PS/2 was introduced into a market in which there were competitors with equal technology and in which there was an $80 000 million installed base of PC-standard software, peripherals, and add-on circuitry with which the PS/2 was not perfectly compatible. It was introduced without its operating system—and thus no software that could take advantage of its capabilities—when 3000 programs were available for the Mac. It is fortunate that the PS/2 had been designed to run the old PC software!

It was perhaps inevitable that the PS/2 would eventually be cloned, especially once Microsoft announced that it would license OS/2 and Presentation Manager. And yet cloning proved easier than might have been expected. IBM's bombastic legal threats were probably calculated to intimidate would-be clones and to raise the expected legal costs that the first clone maker would face. This would present the set of firms interested in cloning with a free rider problem. Each would want another firm to go first so as to ride for free on that firm's legal defence expenditures. This is logical enough, but it did not deter cloning for long.

One predicament that IBM faced was whether to continue producing the old PC models or to cut off production in the hope that doing so would give the PS/2 bandwagon a push. This is a frequent dilemma in the strategy of standards, and IBM chose the latter course. It would appear to have been a mistake. In defence of the move, IBM was earning little on the PC line, and it had high expectations for the PS/2. Nevertheless, at that time, the PS/2 was premature. Its software was not

48

ready, and the incompatible diskettes made converting files and programs tedious even though it was possible.

In addition to these technical problems, the PS/2's reversion to proprietary technology threatened a market that had grown accustomed to open standards. IBM was not subtle in making clear its intention to earn higher margins by tighter control of the PS/2's technology. So for a number of reasons, the market did not follow IBM.

When the PS/2 stumbled, IBM faced its ultimate predicament. Should it encourage clones by licensing the PS/2's technology? As the case closed, the answer seemed to be 'yes'. If licensing did, in fact, draw producers and consumers to the new standard, IBM could then shift its source of rents from a bundled hardware/technology product to technology licensing. Such a change would be consistent with IBM's overall strategy of shifting its source of earnings away from hardware manufacturing to technology and software. Yet this move was obviously defensive, motivated by the fear that the entire PS/2 line was in jeopardy. IBM had to embed the standard before EISA precluded it.

It is interesting to contemplate whether IBM might at this point just give away PS/2 technology. It may be profitable in some circumstances for a firm to do so.[25] The essence of the argument—in the abstract—is that a new product monopolist (i.e. IBM) may profit from delayed competition in a market in which consumers face set-up costs (i.e. investment in the new standard). Potential customers, fearful of being exploited by the monopolist once they make their irrevocable set-up investments, might simply refuse to buy the new product. The monopolist, of course, wants their business and would willingly promise not to exploit their dependence (too much). But how can it make a credible commitment not to do so once customers become locked in? The answer is to license the technology or to pursue a strategy of open architecture.[26] Even though competitors will eventually take much of the market, the firm might still be better off than it would be with a long-term monopoly of a much smaller market.

The revolt of the clones
The case of the Gang of Nine is in some ways analogous to that of the open systems' organizations discussed in Chapter 5. It is a situation in which a number of minor producers are attempting to promote a standard that is an alternative to that promoted by the dominant firm.[27] And one important issue is common to both cases. Who is to lead the group and what are the consequences for the followers? Because

Compaq had done most of the design work on EISA prior to the revolt and because it is number three in the industry (after IBM and Apple), it has assumed the leader's role. If it continues to assume the role (for whatever reason), free rider problems are avoided, but in their place is the problem faced by the other eight of Compaq's growing market power.

The way that the Gang has tried to avoid this problem is an interesting example for other cases. The Gang's members have named a law firm to administer their agreement, they have defined a negotiating process (in which each firm has a veto) to settle disputes, and they have agreed that the specifications for semiconductors implementing EISA will be published so that no single chip producer will have a monopoly. No licence fees are to be paid to Compaq—only an annual $2500 fee will be paid by all members to the law firm for its management of the agreement.

Conclusions

A couple of observations will conclude this chapter on microcomputer standards. First, IBM has apparently recognized that it cannot set a third generation industry-wide standard around the PS/2 and simultaneously defend its proprietary right to that standard. It will have to choose between more intra-standard competition with clones (licensed or otherwise) or more inter-standards competition with Apple, Compaq and the Gang of Nine, and others. IBM seems recently to have chosen more intra-standard competition as the lesser of the two evils, and it is even beginning to encourage the clones. But in so doing, it will lose much of the benefit of setting the standard. Since IBM has claimed in the last few years that it would not remain in the microcomputer field unless margins were improved, one must wonder about the strategy that is intended to achieve higher margins, the veracity of the claim, or IBM's future in the industry.

A related observation is that there is no case evidence in this industry to believe that a firm can use a strategy of open standards to build a large network and then in some way 'close' the standard and exploit that network. When open standards become ubiquitous, they seem also to become a permanent structural feature of an industry.

The third observation is that this industry is now in transition from a period of *de facto* standardization in its second generation to a third generation in which standards are less widespread. The number of competing operating systems is now increasing. A short time ago, only MS/DOS and the Mac's operating system were seen. Now, those two have been joined by OS/2 and UNIX (which is available for microcomputers in variations like Microsoft's XENIX, IBM's AIX, Apple's A/UX, and AT & T's System V). As if that were not enough, Apple announced in mid-1989 the future availability of its System 7.0 which will match the functionality of OS/2 and UNIX with which it is intended to compete directly.

Finally, and perhaps surprisingly, despite the growing number of operating systems, compatibility between the different manufacturers' product lines is becoming more prevalent. The demand for connectivity between different computers is so strong that all firms' products must guarantee it, and in general the new ones do. Operating system software is now so powerful that the different systems can mimic each other. For example, the Mac II can emulate a PC, and the PS/2 offers many of the features of the Mac like pull-down menus and mouse controls. Popular applications software programs for one system are invariably transcribed for others, and the cost of doing so is generally modest. (Typically one-fifth of a program needs to be modified in a transcription.) Furthermore, hardware is sufficiently versatile and memories sufficiently large that individual machines can run different operating systems concurrently. Mac II owners, for example, can switch from the Apple operating system to UNIX with a simple command. One must presume that this trend will continue.

Expressed in other terms, the *de facto* standardization that occurred in the second generation of the industry is breaking down and is being replaced in the third generation by gateways as the dominant means of producing compatibility. And this prompts a number of questions. Is standardization or conversion via gateways the more efficient means of producing compatibility? Right now, these gateways are costly, but that cost is falling while the 'cost' of coordinating different firms' product development surely is not. Secondly, do the various operating systems offer the market real or just spurious variety? It seems at this point that all of these different systems do (or will do) essentially the same thing. Third, will the market accept the proliferating variety of operating systems, tied together as they are by gateways, or will it reject some system standards and insist through its purchases on a return to a world of *de facto* standardization?

Notes and references
1. Microcomputers are roughly defined as computers priced between $500 and $10 000. These approximate limits are intended to exclude inexpensive

'home computers' at the bottom end and sophisticated technical work-stations at the top end.

2. The term 'PC' will be used to designate IBM's microcomputer rather than all microcomputers.

3. A microprocessor is a silicon chip that integrates thousands of electronic components (e.g. transistors and capacitors) into a circuit. The microprocessor functions as the central processing unit of the entire computer.

4. A 'bit' is a binary digit, that is, a 0 or 1. An 8-bit machine accesses and processes data units ('words') that are 8 bits long. A 16-bit machine has a word size twice as long and thus operates much faster and is more powerful. Different generations of microcomputers have been defined on the basis of the word size of their microprocessors: 8-bit machines are first generation, 16-bit machines are second generation, and 32-bit machines are third generation.

5. Machine language refers to program coding written in the binary language of 0s and 1s.

6. An operating system is the software that governs the computer's internal operations, for example, receiving or sending information through the input/output devices, storing data, performing operations, and organizing files. An operating system must be developed to match the hardware of a specific computer or vice versa.

7. Applications software constitutes programs that perform specific functions, for example, word processing, spreadsheet analysis, data management, and games. Each application must be written to match a specific operating system, although they can usually be rewritten to run on other operating systems.

8. CP/M stands for Control Program for Microprocessors.

9. DOS stands for Disk Operating System. Tandy would continue to use its own proprietary operating system until 1984 when it adopted the industry standard MS/DOS.

10. Apple started to produce applications software in-house for the Apple II in 1979, but this accounted for only about 1 per cent of all Apple II software.

11. The company was later renamed VisiCorp.

12. IBM bought 12 per cent of Intel in late 1982 but the two companies were operated independently. In addition to using the Intel microprocessor in its PC, IBM manufactured chips to Intel designs for its larger computers.

13. The PC's keyboard was not the same as IBM's Selectric typewriter, itself an industry standard.

14. 360K storage means that the storage medium can accommodate 360 000 bytes of information. A byte is equal to 8 bits.

15. Hergert, M., Technical standards and competition in the microcomputer industry. In Gabel, L. (ed.), *Product Standardization and Competitive Strategy*, North Holland, Amsterdam, 1987.

16. A hard disk is a large memory internal to the computer. It replaced much of the use of floppy disks.

17. A data bus is the electronic pathway within a computer that allows communication between the computer's different components.
18. Software was not an issue since the PC, PS/2, and Gang of Nine's proposed new system would all run the same programs.
19. In July 1989, IBM and Compaq agreed to license each other's technology. Compaq would pay IBM a fee reported by security analysts to be as much as $100 million to compensate IBM for Compaq's previously unacknowledged use of IBM patents. The agreement also gave Compaq the right to build Micro Channel PS/2 clones.
20. See Farrell, J. and G. Saloner, Standardization and variety, *Economic Letters*, 20, 1986.
21. Jobs's preference for closed architecture dated back to the Apple II. In that case, his preference was overruled by his partner, Steve Wozniak. But with the Apple III, the Lisa, and the Mac, Jobs's preference prevailed (Wozniak had dropped out of the picture at Apple), and thus so did closed architecture. Open architecture would not reappear until Jobs was replaced by Sculley in 1985.
22. *Business Week*, 29 July, 1985, p.71.
23. As this book goes to press, Apple is in the process of radically repositioning its entire product line.
24. Apple sued Microsoft in early 1988 charging infringement of its copyrights on the visual features of its graphical user interface. Microsoft argued that it was licensed in 1985 to use those features with the precursor to Presentation Manager, Windows. At this time, the suit is unresolved.
25. The argument presented here parallels one developed in Farrell, J. and N. Gallini, Second-sourcing as a commitment: Monopoly incentives to attract competition, *Quarterly Journal of Economics*, November 1988.
26. This point is also made by Swann in his study of the microprocessor industry. See Swann, G., Industry microprocessors and the strategy of second-source supply. In Gabel, L. (ed.), *Product Standardization and Competitive Strategy*, North Holland, Amsterdam, 1987.
27. And in both cases we see individual firms—Tandy in the EISA case—that are both members of the revolutionary group and licensees of the dominant technology.

3. The case of video recorders

Introduction

Most readers will be familiar with video cassette recorders (VCRs) and many will also be familiar—possibly from first-hand experience—with the competition between Sony's Betamax and JVC's VHS standards. This chapter will describe and analyse that competition as well as the less well-known competition between alternative standards both before and after Betamax and VHS.

The VCR industry provides an interesting case of standards and competitive strategy because there are episodes in its short history that illustrate most of the important elements of standards competition. For example, the U-Matic format that was introduced in 1970 (and which can still be seen in operation) was an industry-wide and non-proprietary 'open' standard. The competition between Betamax and VHS (and to a lesser extent Philips' V-2000), by contrast, represents at its clearest the nature of competition between incompatible proprietary standards. Furthermore, the strategies that Sony and JVC each used to try to establish its own design as the industry standard are sharply different, and each has been tried often enough in other industries to be properly called 'generic'.

More recently, the 8 mm format reintroduced an industry-wide, non-proprietary standard, although for reasons that will be discussed, many of the major firms in the industry have boycotted it in favour of extending the capabilities of the older VHS format. This competition between two vintages of technology and their associated standards will again illustrate some generic strategy alternatives. The fact that some of the hardware producers also produce software (the pre-recorded tapes) while others do not adds an interesting twist to the logic of the strategies seen in this industry.

The VCR story also illustrates how two or more incompatible standards must be clearly differentiated in order to coexist in a stable equilibrium. Betamax has progressively lost market share to VHS because the larger network of the VHS standard could not be offset by any product features unique to Betamax. Videodisc players, introduced in the early 1980s, failed as well because they were unable to segment the market sufficiently. Finally, the success of the 8 mm standard will depend critically on whether it captures the market segment interested in videography or whether it must displace the well-entrenched VHS standard across all segments of the VCR market.

Finally, and perhaps most importantly, the VCR story shows that to win the battle of standards requires more than just a headstart in the marketplace, and it requires more than just the best product in a purely technical sense. To succeed, firms must understand, either consciously or intuitively, how to assemble all the elements of competitive strategy necessary to establish a standard and then to sustain and exploit it.

Ampex and the first generation of videotape recorders

The technology of videotape recorders (VTRs)[1] was first commercialized successfully in 1956 by an American company named Ampex Corporation. Ampex's technological strength was in magnetic tape recording of sound and data with applications in science, the military, and industry. The company had been growing at a compound annual rate of 70 per cent for half a dozen years prior to its introduction of a VTR, and by 1956 it had $10 million in annual sales and 800 employees.

Ampex's—and others'—interest in the technology of videotaping was stimulated by the rapid growth of the television industry. In 1951, 11 million US households had TV sets, half a million sets were being sold monthly, and coast-to-coast network transmission was not far off. The television industry needed a means of recording programmes broadcast on the East Coast for later transmission on the West Coast. Magnetic recording technology, a technology in which Ampex was a leader, seemed to many experts to be the most appropriate. The best alternative— Kinescope—was a photographic technology, and although its picture quality was acceptable, it was too complex and costly to be satisfactory.

Thus, the first sales of VTRs were to TV broadcasters, and Ampex's introduction of its VT-1000 in 1956 was to those affiliated with CBS. Later sales of prototypes were to NBC and ABC. The machine used two-inch wide tape and sold for about $45 000.

Ampex's earliest models experienced some serious production problems. Their recording heads had a lifetime of only 100 hours and could not be mass produced with sufficient quality to ensure their interchangeability in recording units in field use. The problem was eventually solved, however, and Ampex slowly built up its sales. By mid-1959, it had sold 375 VTRs. By 1961, it had sold nearly 900, which constituted 75 per cent of all VTR sales world-wide.

The next challenge to Ampex was to achieve colour compatibility in a VTR. This was done by a patent sharing agreement with RCA.[2] The patent agreement gave RCA access to the Ampex technology embodied in the VT-1000 while Ampex got RCA's colour technology. Ampex introduced the first colour converter kit for its VT-1000 in 1958, and RCA introduced its first VTR in 1959. By 1961, RCA had 25 per cent of the market and Ampex the rest.

The next stage of development of the Ampex VTR was the switch from vacuum tubes to solid state electronics. Ampex was pushed into a technology sharing agreement with Sony, a leader in the application of transistors to small consumer electronic products,[3] in order to forestall the obvious threat that RCA would come to dominate the market. Sony was to get access to Ampex's patented VTR technology, and Ampex would get both Sony's transistor technology and a Japanese partner to manufacture in Japan for sales to both Japan and the Far East. (The policy of the Japanese Ministry of International Trade and Industry (MITI) at the time insisted that all foreign firms manufacturing in Japan did so cooperatively with a Japanese firm.)

Sony did assist Ampex in developing a transistorised VTR—the VT-1100. But further cooperation ended in 1961 with a dispute over the royalties due on Sony's use of Ampex's technology and over a disagreement about the feasibility of some of Ampex's technology. As a consequence, Ampex abandoned plans to manufacture in Japan in cooperation with Sony. In 1964, Ampex tried again with a different Japanese partner—Toshiba. In 1964, Toamco, their joint venture company, started to produce Ampex-designed VTRs for the Japanese broadcast market.

Early attempts to identify a mass market

Ampex was aware from the very beginning that a nascent mass consumer product might be lying in its hands. The president of the company, George Long, was quoted in 1956 as having said that 'eventually [VTRs] might be mass-produced for home use by persons who want to see a programme over and over again or want it recorded during their absence'.[4] Others showed similar prescience: 'A more visionary project is the thought of a home recorder and playback for taped TV pictures. Why not pick up the new full-length motion picture at the corner drugstore and then run it through one's home TV receiver?'[5]

By the mid-1960s, the vision of a mass market VTR was coming into better focus, and Ampex was beginning to plan products for it. To succeed, a mass market VTR would need to be much less expensive than the existing VTRs, and this implied among other things a wider industry standard with which to exploit production economies of scale and learning. Unfortunately, as a result of a conflict between departments, each claiming the right to the VTR's development, Ampex introduced two incompatible VTRs simultaneously (the basic technology of each was different), one called the VR-303 and the other the VR-3000. Neither was a practical mass market product. The VR-303 was quickly abandoned and the VR-3000 was marketed to industrial and educational customers.

After this experience trying to sell two incompatible technologies to the same market, the company next attempted to serve two different markets with a single standard. By halving the writing speed of its high quality professional equipment—equipment using one-inch wide tape—Ampex tried to develop a new product for what was destined to be an elusive mass consumer market.

Ampex introduced the prototype of its VR-7000 in Chicago in June 1965. But a price of $1500 with another $500 for a camera put it beyond the reach of any latent mass market. It suffered from two other problems as well. Colour TV had just appeared, but the VR-7000 was black-and-white. And it was complex to use since its tape was 'open reel' rather than housed within a cassette. Ampex introduced a slightly less expensive VR-6000, which was compatible with the VR-7000, yet it too failed to develop mass appeal.

The market problems that Ampex faced were not unique to it. Sony, too, was trying to produce a VTR for the mass market and had been continually working on VTRs since its break-up with Ampex in 1961. In 1964, it demonstrated its first model, also black-and-white, called the CV-2000. It was unsuccessful, but its use of half-inch tape presaged the tape width standard that would eventually succeed.

At a major trade show in the summer of 1966, six manufacturers displayed VTRs. The conclusion they all reached was that a mass market VTR would require colour recording, a tape cassette, and high reliability. They also reached the conclusion that the technology to achieve all this at a price that would have to be substantially lower than those currently quoted was not yet available. Nevertheless, VTRs were selling successfully to schools, hospitals, and factories, and Ampex's sales were running about 400 units monthly at the end of 1966.

57

By late 1967, the audio-visual equipment market was worth about $15 million annually, and there were a number of incompatible products serving it. In value terms, Ampex held 50 per cent of the total although it held a minority share by units. This was because Ampex's one-inch tape was the standard of the high quality professional market, which constituted 70 per cent of the total market by value. The less expensive half-inch tape models sold only by Japanese firms went to less sophisticated consumers who constituted a minority of the value of the market but the majority of the units sold. (A few firms, like Sony, sold both half-inch and one-inch tape models.)

The year 1966 turned out to be the zenith of Ampex's line of VTRs. After that, it lost ground to the half-inch tape models sold by the Japanese. Although they were all incompatible with each other, these half-inch tape machines were more compact and less expensive than Ampex's one-inch tape models, and thus they were superior for all but professional customers. Ampex had become trapped and handicapped by its dedication to a single one-inch tape standard.

Instavideo

By 1968, Ampex had been driven into a complete re-evaluation of its marketing strategy. The core of the re-evaluation was an analysis of the various uses to which VTRs might be put. Ampex identified three such uses. The first was called *repetitive viewing*. This could consist, for example, of training films that would be professionally made and then copied for field use. The professional quality master would be on high quality, one-inch tape, and the copies could be made on lower quality, half-inch tapes for viewing on inexpensive half-inch format VTRs. The second use was called *instantaneous response*. This was the opposite of repetitive viewing. Instantaneous response implied filming and immediate viewing in the same location. Instantaneous response required portability, reliability, ease of use, and low cost. The presumption was that the user was not a professional film producer. Applications were imagined in education, business, and households. Finally, there was *semi-repetitive viewing* which involved a mix of the other two uses.

From its analysis, Ampex concluded for the first time that the professional market and a mass consumer market could not be served by the same tape width standard. Half-inch tapes did not have the storage capacity to provide the picture quality that professionals required. But one-inch tape necessitated a larger and more expensive machine than the mass market would accept. In short, Ampex realized that standardization on its professional one-inch tape implied too great a loss in functionality for the mass market.[6]

Having learned its lesson, Ampex set out to develop a new standard that would be defined by what the mass market wanted, and then developed into a family of compatible products specifically for that market. The product line was called *Instavideo*. The budget for *Instavideo* was $1.5 million. Ampex's attention was focused on home programming and the development of a suitable camera/recorder system for it. Home programming, which later became known as *videography*, was one part of the instantaneous response market. Although it would be targeted at home programming, Instavideo was also expected to be suited to the needs of two other market segments that Ampex identified. These two (which would eventually dominate home programming) were recording and later playback of TV programmes (called *time-shift* TV recording) and the play of professionally pre-recorded tapes such as feature movies.

In a concurrent but unrelated development, the Electronics Industry of Japan formally adopted in the autumn of 1969 a standard half-inch magnetic videotape (first demonstrated by Sony)—the EIAJ Type 1 standard. Ampex chose to adopt this standard for Instavideo, and its decision was considered to be particularly important to the software industry where the lack of a common standard inhibited the production of pre-recorded films. Unfortunately, Ampex's decision to adopt the Type 1 standard was coupled with a decision to use a different cassette size from that of the Japanese firms. So whereas there was now an international standard for tape, the distribution network—and consumers—would still face incompatible products because of incompatible cassettes.

Instavideo was demonstrated for the first time in September 1970. The portable recorder weighed about 16 lb (7kg) with its batteries, and the camera weighed 5 lb (2 kg) more. The system of recorder/player and camera was to be priced at $800 for black-and-white and $1500 for colour. The colour recorder/player alone would cost $1000. The date of availability was to be January 1972. Sales were expected to represent between 40 and 50 per cent of a total market of about 30 000 VTRs in 1973. Forecast sales for 1974 were $7 million.

The press reaction to Instavideo's introduction was lauditory. As examples of press comments: 'There is a tremendous virtue in an agreed-upon standard for the great majority of users who are more interested in the interchange of information (software) than they are in the world's best S/N, time based stability, and resolution features. When left to the engineers, such things never seem to get out of the laboratory'.[7] 'Instavideo might well become the "genesis" standard that will make VTR truly a big business'.[8]

When Instavideo was announced, three Japanese firms—Sony, JVC, and Matsushita—and one European firm—Philips—were also working on magnetic videotape technology. As a recording medium, magnetic tape entailed readily available material and a well-understood technology. And it was the only medium that was erasable and reusable. This would, of course, be a decisive advantage if VTRs were to be used extensively for home programming or recording. The big disadvantage of magnetic tape was that it was expensive to make large numbers of pre-recorded tape copies since each tape had to be individually copied from a master.

In addition to the firms mentioned above, RCA and CBS were also active in the industry, although they were working on non-magnetic tape technologies. No two firms' products, actual or under development, were compatible.

The major players
The companies that play a continuing role in this story are detailed below.

SONY
Sony was established in 1946 and was the world leader in transistorized products in the 1950s. It also had expertise in miniaturization. It was a relatively undiversified company and the first Japanese firm to make colour TVs without an RCA licence. As was noted above, Sony first introduced a VTR in 1964. In 1969, it demonstrated (although it did not market) a cassette-based, half-inch colour model which was the first complete VCR system. At the end of the decade, Sony offered 15 different VTR models. The company was particularly noted for its product development and product quality. With significance for the VCR story, Sony was one of the few Japanese firms to market almost exclusively under its own name rather than under original equipment marketing (OEM) contracts.

JVC
JVC (Victor Company of Japan) was a majority-owned division of Matsushita, which purchased it in 1953. Despite the ownership link, however, the two companies operated independently. JVC started research on VTRs in 1955 and displayed a prototype in 1961. That

prototype was priced at $14 990 compared to Ampex's price of $41 950 and RCA's of $59 500. The company's first commercialized VTR was sold in 1963. In 1971, when JVC joined Sony and Matsushita in adopting the U-Matic standard, the company began a development programme that was to result in the VHS system. The first VHS prototype was built in 1972.

JVC had the weakest marketing and distribution network of all the major Japanese consumer electronics firms and thus was mostly an OEM producer.

MATSUSHITA

Mastsushita was the largest and most diversified Japanese maker of home electrical and electronic products. In 1968, Matsushita had 32 000 product lines compared to 70—80 at Sony. Its strengths were in manufacturing, marketing, and distribution rather than in product development, and it sold under many brand names including Panasonic, Quasar, and Technics. Matsushita started work on VTRs under a grant from MITI in 1958, and its first commercial VTR was introduced in 1964.

N. V. PHILIPS

Philips was a pioneer in the European VCR industry and developed its first professional market model, the N-1500, in 1970. That model was adapted and sold in the household consumer market in the mid-1970s, but Philips' most significant consumer VCR, called the V-2000, was not introduced until 1979. It will be discussed in detail below as will Philips' development of a laser-based system.

RCA

RCA had a tradition of technological research and was a leader in the development of colour TV that began to establish itself in the market in the 1960s. RCA differed from most of the other firms in the industry in that it had a financial interest in broadcasting through its subsidiary NBC, and it had significant copyright holdings from another subsidiary, RCA Records. Thus, it was able to offer both software and technology.

RCA's first VTR was introduced in 1959 as a result of the Ampex/ RCA collaboration mentioned previously. By 1970, all of RCA's consumer video recording development work—including the use of laser technology for both tape and disc recording—was grouped together under the brand name *SelectaVision*.

61

When RCA abandoned its computer business in 1971 and took a $250 million write-off, it cut its investment in SelectaVision and completely abandoned all magnetic videotape development. It reasoned that tapes would never achieve the industry-wide standardization necessary to a mass market product (despite the Japanese inter-firm agreement) and that prices would remain too high for mass market appeal. Furthermore, RCA was having trouble with the development of colour capability with its tape machines. All of RCA's efforts were refocused on a different technology and product—the SelectaVision videodisc.

SelectaVision videodisc was only able to play pre-recorded software. Thus, it was suited to only one segment of the market—viewing purchased or rented pre-recorded films. Those interested in time-shift TV viewing or videography would have to use another device. For pre-recorded films, however, it had a potential advantage in that copies of discs could be cheaply stamped from a master disc rather than tediously transcribed from a master tape.

CBS

CBS, like RCA, had significant software copyrights. And, like RCA, it focused its efforts on an alternative to magnetic videotape recording. In 1970, it introduced a colour tape system (based on photographic technology) called EVR (*Electronic Video Recording*) that, like the RCA videodisc, was only able to play pre-recorded software. To make the equipment, CBS licensed nine manufacturers including Matsushita, Hitachi, Toshiba, and Mitsubishi.

Although EVR was originally intended for households, its eventual price of around $800 (compared to forecast prices of less than $300) forced CBS to retarget it for educational and business use. This made impossible the hope that EVR could be built directly into a TV set with consequent savings in manufacturing costs. EVR was discontinued in January 1972 with a $30 million write-off after only a year in production.

The U-Matic standard

In late 1970, Sony, JVC, and Matsushita, worried about Philips' N-1500 in Europe and fearful that RCA's SelectaVision and CBS's EVR would threaten future acceptance of their cassettes for the home VTR market, met and set another standard tape and cassette size called the *U-Matic*. The standard, originating with Sony, was a three-quarter-inch tape, a cassette size of 22.1 × 14 × 3.2 cm, and 60 minutes of recording time.

U-Matic VCRs were first marketed by Sony in 1969 at a price of about $1000, and the U-Matic subsequently became an important standard for professional use. But the cassette was too large for home use.

Early attempts to standardize industry

The profusion of technologies and standards outlined above not surprisingly raised industry concern about incompatibility and the need for an industry agreement on a common standard.

Since VTRs did not use the public airwaves or telecommunications network, no public regulatory body had jurisdiction over the industry or the authority to impose a standard. Standarization, should it occur, would have to come from the voluntary agreement of the firms in the industry.

The International Tape Association (ITA) held conferences in Cannes in 1971 and 1972 with standards on the agenda. At the 1971 conference, there were 1319 representatives from 645 companies and 31 countries. They represented 15 alternative standards for four different technological approaches. The keynote speech was given by Stanley Gortikov, the President of Capital Records, who warned that the VTR industry would have to resolve the standarization problem before it would be ready for the consumer market.

Mr Gortikov said that if he were a consumer, he would ask the producers,

If you do entice me into buying one of your black boxes, do you guarantee me availability of a full range of recorded material two years from now? Five years from now? Do I run the risk of your hardware being obsoleted by a more popular configuration? [If I am a retailer], am I going to have to stock a separate and different cartridge library for every hardware configuration that you guys decide to come out with? Will my customers be able to buy a specific Broadway show, for example, for only one configuration because it is not licensed for all others? Or even worse, will I have to stock that show in six different configurations just because you all can't get together on compatibility?[9]

Peter Gruber of Columbia Pictures argued that the reluctance to accept standards sprang from the enormous spending of each firm on

63

research and development to produce the first (incompatible) models and prototypes. At that point, he argued, agreement on a single standard cassette would reward one firm and penalize the others whose cassette sizes were not chosen.

A strong plea for standards also came from a spokesperson for Philips, who pointed out that Philips was far ahead of firms in both the United States and Japan on agreements on standards. The company had reached agreements already with Telefunken, Blaupunkt, Grundig, Saba, Thorn Electric, and a number of smaller firms.

But not all the participants were enthusiastic about standardization, at least not immediately. Spokespeople for both Matsushita and Sony argued that a three-quarter-inch tape like U-Matic might hold a significant advantage over the EIAJ Type 1 half-inch standard. One should be aware, the Matsushita spokesperson warned, that 'as the cartridge-type VTR has never been sold in the market, we are not fully aware of the customer's need, for example, as to shape, size, and playing time.'[10] Even some users were wary. A representative from *Time-Life* said that his company believed in 'natural selection'[11] to decide on a tape standard.

The 1971 conference ended with the appointment of a three-man temporary organizing committee charged with setting up an 'International Council on Standards' under the auspices of the ITA.

At the start of the follow-up 1972 conference, it was known that deliveries would soon start of four incompatible video tapes—CBS's photographic-based EVR, and magnetic VCRs from Sony, Philips, and AVCO.[12] Standarization was thus generally acknowledged to be a lost cause, and although a third conference was scheduled for 1973, it was clear that market competition would determine which tape standard would ultimately prevail.

The end of Instavideo and Ampex

By 1972, Instavideo was still not available for sale due to a series of manufacturing problems in the Toamco plant where it was made for both Ampex and Toshiba. And as the scheduled date of sale slipped further and further into the future, Ampex began to doubt its own strategy for the line.

First, Ampex feared the consequences of the industry's continuing failure to set a common standard. The three-quarter-inch U-Matic standard had been introduced in violation of the EIAJ agreement, and the cassette sizes were different between different producers within the

EIAJ half-inch standard. Ampex was still making one-inch tape models, but they were positioned for the professional quality market.

Furthermore, various incompatible playback-only systems were on the market. And although Ampex thought that they would fail for lack of enough pre-recorded software, this view was not universally held. At the very least, the playback-only systems would cannibalize sales from the VTRs.

Secondly, and more fundamental, Ampex doubted that the still-elusive mass market was yet in sight and that Instavideo would be well suited to it when it did appear. The basic problem was that no one yet knew what household consumers would want a VTR for. If the overwhelming use was to be viewing pre-recorded films, then RCA and CBS, with their specialized equipment and large libraries of copyright films, would be the best positioned. But if time-shift TV viewing and videography proved important—even if not dominant—uses, consumers might prefer the more versatile VTRs to playback-only equipment.

The potential for Instavideo might have looked brighter to Ampex had the company been able to provide the software that would be required by the household consumers interested in viewing pre-recorded films. Ampex did, in fact, produce and distribute blank and pre-recorded magnetic tape for the consumer audio market. But unlike for RCA or CBS, these were not core businesses for Ampex.

With concern about the lack of standards and a growing fear that a mass market might still be a few years off, Ampex's best strategy was to try to market Instavideo as a stand-alone system that did not need a network of standards and an inventory of software in order to function. Ampex decided to target Instavideo to institutions in business, law enforcement, medicine, and education.

Unfortunately, Ampex was to suffer near bankruptcy in 1972 as a result of financial overexpansion. From being one of the glamour stocks in the decade of the 1960s, Ampex lost $12 million in 1971 and $90 million in 1972. Faced with continuing manufacturing and development problems and the need for substantial further investment in VTRs were it to succeed, Ampex abandoned Instavideo in October 1972 before it ever came into production. Since Ampex's failure, no American firm has made VCRs.[13]

Betamax, VHS, and the mass consumer market

Sony started in the early 1970s to develop a cassette-playing videotape recorder for the mass consumer market, and by mid-1974, the company began experimental production of the *Betamax*. But Sony's target market was not the same as Ampex's had been. The Betamax was intended principally for time-shifting TV recording. This led Sony to design its VCR with a one-hour recording capacity—seemingly satisfactory for its planned use.

Sony was well aware of the seriousness of the standardization issues that had until then cursed the industry, and it wanted access to Matsushita's huge domestic and overseas marketing network that would be vital to the Betamax's launch. In September 1974, Sony representatives met with those of Matsushita and JVC to try to convince them to license Sony's proprietary Betamax standard. JVC, at work on what was to become the rival to Betamax, never looked at Sony's equipment. Matsushita did, but claimed (rightly, in retrospect) that Betamax's one-hour playing time was too short. Like JVC, however, Matsushita was working on another proprietary standard—the VX-2000—that was incompatible with the standards of both Sony and JVC. So Sony introduced the Betamax alone in April 1975, and production of 10 000 units monthly started from a greenfield plant in Japan.

JVC tried to form its own standards alliance with the cooperation of Matsushita, Sanyo, Toshiba, Hitachi, Sharp, and Mitsubishi. But JVC's VHS (*Video Home System*) line was not yet ready for production, and Matsushita, Sanyo, and Toshiba were all still developing their own proprietary—and incompatible—standards. (Sanyo and Toshiba actually introduced VCRs in 1975.) Only Sharp and Mitsubishi took VHS licences. Hitachi followed later when Sony refused its request to license Betamax.

Sony and JVC appealed to MITI in mid-1976 to mediate the growing standards division. Neither company was willing to compromise, however, and MITI proved unable to end the battle. Each firm was willing to license the other (and its allies) to use its technology, but neither wanted to abandon its own development. MITI's one modest accomplishment was to get Sanyo and Toshiba to withdraw their products (although this may have been because of their technological inferiority rather than because of a desire for industry-wide standardization). But since JVC was not yet ready to produce VHS units in volume (and possibly because Matsushita had not yet adopted VHS), both Sanyo and Toshiba adopted Betamax.

In October 1976, JVC started to sell VHS equipment and to supply Hitachi and Sharp. In January 1977, Matsushita dropped its VX-2000 under pressure from the industry and licensed the VHS technology.[14]

So the industry was split into two camps, and competition between the two has been its dominant characteristic ever since. In the Betamax camp with Sony were Sanyo and Toshiba. In JVC's VHS camp were Matsushita, Hitachi, Mitsubishi, and Sharp.

With its 18-month headstart in the market, Sony management felt that it could pre-empt JVC and the VHS. In 1976 and 1977, Sony had over 50 per cent of the VCR market. But Sony's small domestic retail network proved a major disadvantage relative to its competitors in the Japanese market, which was the first to develop. Sony had a network of about 13 500 affiliated retailers and cooperating stores in the late 1970s. Matsushita had about 30 000 distributors. Sony tried to increase its market share by distributing through discount stores in major cities in Japan, yet by the end of 1978, Sony's production share had fallen to 27.9 per cent and Matsushita's share had risen to 35.8 per cent.

Sony was at a disadvantage in Japan due to its relatively smaller distribution networks there, but the biggest challenge was to come in the United States. In February 1977, Zenith announced that it would sell Betamax machines (made by Sony) under the Zenith name. A month later, RCA decided to sell VHS machines (made by Matsushita). RCA's choice was due to VHS's longer play time. RCA wanted a four-hour recording capacity, principally to allow the recording of football games. VHS could achieve this by halving tape playing speed. But the picture quality of Betamax was too badly impaired by the slower speed for Sony to follow. So Zenith and RCA went separate directions, and their decisions set off a scramble for licences in the United States.

Magnavox and GTE Sylvania joined RCA the same year as retailers of Matsushita-made VCRs that each sold under its own label. Sears, however, contracted for Betamax VCRs from Sanyo (which was making 80 per cent of Sears' colour TVs at the time).

The RCA/VHS and Zenith/Betamax competition in the United States was critical to both the companies and the standards. RCA and Zenith were the two biggest US colour TV sellers, each with more than 20 per cent of that market (see Table 3.1), and each had big distribution and service networks.

With the appearance of suitable products, the long-awaited mass consumer market developed rapidly despite the competing standards. World-wide demand passed 1 million units annually in 1978 and doubled each year of the five-year period from 1976 to 1981. By the mid-1980s, annual sales exceeded 30 million units.

67

Table 3.1   Per cent of US color TV Market and VCR standard, 1976

Company (brand)	Market share (%)	Standard
Zenith	23	Beta
RCA	20	VHS
Sears	9	Beta and VHS
Magnavox	6	VHS
Matsushita (Panasonic)	3	VHS
Matsushita (Quasar)	5	VHS
General Electric	6	VHS
Sony	7	Beta
Montgomery Ward	2	VHS
Sanyo	1	Beta
Hitachi	1	VHS
Sharp	2	VHS
J. C. Penny	1	VHS
Toshiba	1	Beta

Source: Hariharan, S., Technological compatibility, standards and global competition: The dynamics of industry evolution and competitive strategies, unpublished Ph.D. dissertation, University of Michigan, 1990.

RCA and VHS slowly displaced Zenith and Betamax by virtue of longer play time, a bigger marketing campaign (RCA spent $4 million in promotion in the last quarter of 1977, including free pre-recorded tape give-aways with purchases), and lower prices. Zenith's launch price for Betamax was $1300 and RCA's for the VHS system was $995. Sony followed with price cuts but was generally the more expensive of the two alternatives in the first few years (see Table 3.2).

Sony was eventually able to counter the advantage that VHS held in recording time. It lengthened play time repeatedly from an original one hour to two in 1977 and eventually to six hours, although by then play time had ceased to be a competitive issue.

Sony introduced stereo audio capability in its Betamax in an effort to differentiate it from VHS, but Matsushita soon followed. Stereo constituted only 4 per cent of the United States market in 1982 and 8 per cent in 1983, but its share slowly rose to about 20 per cent in the mid-1980s. (Questions of compatibility did not arise with stereo since existing cassettes could be used in the new equipment.)

The US market grew rapidly in the 1980s although it lagged the Japanese market by about a year. Market penetration rose from 1.5 per cent in 1979 to 7.9 per cent in 1982 and 18.5 per cent in 1984. A major reason for the rapid market penetration was that excess inventories in

Table 3.2 VCR prices (inflation-corrected 1976 US dollars)

Year	Beta price (US $)	VHS price (US $)
1976	1200	—
1977	1070	822
1978	816	755
1979	701	710
1980	586	607
1981	480	503
1982	412	383
1983	350	321

Source: Hariharan, S., Technological compatibility, standards and global competition: The dynamics of industry evolution and competitive strategies, unpublished Ph.D. dissertation, University of Michigan, 1990.

1980–1981 and a recession in 1981–1982 led to price reductions in what proved to be a price elastic market.

Another factor accounting for the rapid increase in market penetration was the increasing supply of pre-recorded tapes. In the later 1970s, the supply of pre-recorded software was not a competitive variable since few pre-recorded tapes were available for either Betamax or VHS. Thus, VCRs were used principally for time-shift TV viewing. But supply of pre-recorded tapes started to rise rapidly in the 1980s. In 1983, there were 9.5 million pre-recorded tapes sold in the United States and 14.5 million in 1984. Soon, the play of pre-recorded tapes constituted 50 per cent of VCR usage in the United States. This rising usage of pre-recorded tapes proved another disadvantage to Sony since it came at the time of relative decline in Sony's installed base (see Table 3.3), and rental stores preferred to stock the more popular VHS tapes.

In a downward spiral, Sony's loss of sales market share (Table 3.4) prompted former Betamax loyalists like Toshiba and Zenith to switch to VHS.

Philips' V-2000
Philips introduced its V-2000 in Europe in 1979. The V-2000 was incompatible with all the other VCRs then on the market. The sound and picture quality of the V-2000 were generally recognized as superior to those of either the VHS or the Betamax, and the V-2000 had an eight-hour play time. The model was more complex to manufacture,

Table 3.3   VCR installed base in the United States (in thousands of units; percentages given in parentheses)

Year	Beta (%)	VHS (%)	Total
1976	70 (100)	—	70
1977	283 (88)	38 (12)	321
1978	428 (58)	307 (42)	735
1979	623 (51)	600 (49)	1223
1980	904 (45)	1121 (55)	2025
1981	1198 (34)	2299 (66)	3497

Source: Grindley, P. and R. McBryde, Using product standards in business strategy: The case of video cassette recorders, unpublished manuscript, London Business School, 1989.

however, and Philips immediately experienced serious reliability problems with it.

Philips licensed its technology to other firms in Europe, but it was unsuccessful in spreading it to the United States. Its subsidiary, North American Philips, refused the V-2000 because in its view it was too expensive. Philips did not establish any alternative US marketing channels.

Cursed with a complex technology and a domestic European market within which there were incompatible TV standards, Philips found itself

Table 3.4   VCR market shares (in per cent of units sold)

Year	Beta share (%)	VHS share (%)
1976	100.0	0.0
1977	84.9	15.1
1978	31.1	68.9
1979	31.0	69.0
1980	28.0	72.0
1981	25.3	74.7
1982	24.1	75.9
1983	22.3	77.7
1984	20.6	79.4
1985	12.4	87.6
1986	9.5	90.0
1987	4.6	93.1

Source: Hariharan, S., Technological compatibility, standards and global competition: The dynamics of industry evolution and competitive strategies, unpublished Ph.D. dissertation, University of Michigan, 1990.

a high cost producer in a price sensitive industry. The V-2000 sold for 20–30 per cent more than other VCRs.

Later models of Philips' VCRs were more reliable, but they were still not as popular as the VHS and Betamax, and the small network of users meant that the selection of pre-recorded tapes for the V-2000 was relatively small. This was especially unfortunate because the play of pre-recorded tapes came to constitute 75 per cent of VCR usage in Europe. This surprised Philips which had intended its VCR to be used for time-shift TV viewing. VHS had a big advantage in the pre-recorded tape market due to the partnership with Thorn which dominated the UK rental market with its Radio Rentals subsidiary.

Philips' share of the European VCR market started to fall rapidly in 1977 when the VHS arrived. In 1978, VHS had already taken 38 per cent of the market. By 1983, VHS accounted for between two-thirds and three-quarters of European VCR sales, Betamax for one-fifth, and the V-2000 for the remainder. Nationally, the V-2000 had less than 2 per cent of the UK market but 15–25 per cent of the West German, Belgian, Italian, and Dutch markets.

Facing a falling market for the V-2000, in 1982 Philips and Grundig (which made the V-2000 under licence) filed an anti-dumping case in the European Commission (EC) against Japanese VCR exporters. This was the largest anti-dumping suit in the history of EC–Japanese relations. The result was a three-year voluntary export restraint (VER) agreement dating from early 1983. The VER limited annual Japanese exports to 4 million finished units and 600 000 kits to be assembled in Europe by European and Japanese firms. In 1984, the limit for kits was raised to 1.1 million. The VER covered prices as well as market shares, with market shares fixed at their historical levels. The idea was to leave Philips and Grundig a protected market of about 1.2 million units (although in the end they never sold their quotas).

The EC–Japanese VER had a number of consequences. The first was to increase the market share of the VHS standard. With quantity restricted by the VER, the Japanese exporters decided to concentrate on just one standard—the relatively more popular VHS—instead of both Betamax and VHS. And with the restricted supply caused by the VER, the price of Japanese VCRs rose by about $100, raising in turn the profits for the Japanese.

Another consequence of the VER was to induce Japanese firms to begin to produce VCRs in Europe. Some of the Japanese firms had TV manufacturing facilities in Europe that were switched to producing

VCRs. For example, Sony had a wholly owned West German subsidiary called Vega that produced Betamax. Sanyo, Mitsubishi, Toshiba, and Sharp made VHS units in the United Kingdom. JVC licensed production to Thompson-Brandt and formed a joint venture with AEG-Telefunken and Thorn-EMI called J2T. Matsushita licensed Bosch.

After a 1983 loss of $55 million on its own VCRs, Philips announced that it would make the VHS machines under licence along with the V-2000.[15] Philips eventually abandoned the V-2000 completely.

VCRs versus videodiscs

Industry experts in the late 1970s felt that three distinctly different market segments existed in the broadly defined video recording industry. One was for time-shift TV viewing. The second was for home production. The third was for viewing pre-recorded films. The question that had no clear answer at the time was whether consumers would prefer a single VCR for all three uses or two different products—a VCR for time-shift TV viewing and home production and a specialized product for viewing pre-recorded films.

For time-shift TV viewing, the VCR was naturally positioned. This was the segment at which Sony had targeted its Betamax in the first place. And in home movie production, the VCR had devastated the market for 8 mm photographic systems. Sales of 1 million 8 mm photographic cameras in 1972 fell to 100 000 by 1982. Although VCR hardware was more expensive (in 1977, the cheapest VCR camera cost $260), the film was so much cheaper (the cost of one hour of filming using 8 mm film was $175 compared to $8 for magnetic tape) that the total cost could be much less. Furthermore, the movie was immediately available, there was no need for a special projector and screen, less light was needed to record, movies could be of longer duration, and the magnetic tape was reusable. Finally, households with libraries of 8 mm films could have them professionally transcribed on to magnetic tape.

Whether the VCR was well positioned for the play of pre-recorded films was the open question. For this, many felt that playback-only videodisc machines were better suited than magnetic tape cassette players. Discs offered superior picture quality and lower software price. Furthermore, the firms that were developing the VCR market had no arrangement with the entertainment industry, whereas firms like RCA and CBS, which controlled the copyrights to the software, were concentrating on the specialized videodisc hardware.

Philips was the only firm to produce both a VCR and a playback-only videodisc system, called Laserdisc. The V-2000 was to be for time-shift TV viewing while Laserdisc would serve the market for viewing pre-recorded films. Like the standard embodied in the V-2000, the standard created by Laserdisc was based on Philips' proprietary technology. Philips hoped that the lower software production costs with a disc would induce producers to develop material specifically for it. It calculated that a disc producer could break-even with sales of only 10 000 to 30 000 copies compared to a required market penetration of 20 million homes for a TV programme to break-even.

The first of a number of incompatible videodisc machines to appear on the market was Magnavox's Magnavision in December 1978. Its price was $700. Thus, the videodisc hardware price was cheaper than that of the VCRs, but the choice of pre-recorded film titles was very small. In 1979, there were only 200 movie titles listed for Magnavision. RCA's SelectaVision and Pioneer's LaserVision were introduced after Magnavision. Prices for pre-recorded films ran between $5.95 and $15.95. JVC introduced its VHD (Video High Density) disc system in 1983, although it was sold mostly in Japan.

All of the videodisc systems were commercially unsuccessful, but the technology was subsequently used to develop the digital audio disc (the CD).

The market for camcorders

As the VHS standard came to dominate the VCR market,[16] a new venue of competition developed. As was explained previously, the VCR was targeted in part at households making home movies. But despite being overwhelmingly superior to the photographic technology it displaced, the VCR was not really well designed for the specific needs of that market. It was not sufficiently portable.

With the earliest vintage of VCR, the camera had to be linked to the non-portable VCR by a cable. Thus, filming had to be done from immediately beside the VCR. Portability was first achieved in 1980 by separating the VCR into its two parts—the recorder and the tuner/timer. A user only needed to carry the camera and recorder (and its battery pack), which was connected to the camera by a cable. By 1981, the weight and bulk of the entire VCR (recorder and tuner/timer) were reduced sufficiently so that it could be carried, and Sony sold a Betamax-format model in 1982. Subsequent Betamax and VHS models became progressively lighter, but the half-inch format portables were still undesirably heavy.

So a ready market existed in the early 1980s for the first firms to develop a compact and more portable product specifically intended for videography. The technique to do so was to combine both the camera and the recorder into a single unit called a *camcorder*.

There were a couple of advantages to combining the camera and the recording unit. The user need carry just a single unit rather than two pieces connected by a cable. And production costs could be reduced significantly. The critical technical challenge was to ensure that the camcorder was light enough to be held still while filming.

The competitive question that quickly surfaced was whether the camcorder would be based on an existing tape standard or on a new miniature standard better suited to videography. Two other important questions faced the camcorder. Would the product find a mass market at prices feasible with the available technology? This would be a minimum of $700. And would the available technology—magnetic recording—be the best long-term approach to electronic imaging? Other technologies such as silicon chip imaging were thought to be longer-term alternatives.

The 8 mm agreement

In 1981, an *ad hoc* group of five VCR makers—Sony, Hitachi, JVC, Matsushita, and Philips—met to discuss an 8 mm miniature standard for videography and possibly for the next generation of VCRs. The five firms accounted for 70 per cent of all VCR sales. Sony, which had exhibited an 8 mm home movie system in 1980, provided the impetus for the talks that were conducted under the auspices of the Japanese Electronics Industry Association. Draft standards were completed in 1982, and in March 1983, 127 manufacturers (including 97 Japanese firms) signed an agreement of standardization.

Details of the 8 mm agreement included the following:

- An 8 mm tape width (slightly less than two-thirds the width of the VHS half-inch tape) and a standardized cassette (half the size of the VHS cassette or about the size of an audio tape cassette).
- Maximum play length of 1.5 hours for the NTSC TV standard (used in North America and Japan) and 1 hour for the PAL TV standard (used in Western Europe except for France).
- Metal-coated tapes rather than metal oxides.
- A recording process that would permit the recording of digital stereo sound.

Although the 8 mm agreement might seem to imply that for the first time virtually all the firms in the market would offer consumers full system compatibility, such was not the case. There was and still is uncertainty about the implementation of the standard.

One view was that since all makers signed the agreement, they would all abide by it. The 8 mm standard would therefore become the universal standard for camcorders and the next generation of VCRs, replacing both VHS and Betamax. Some industry experts forecasted sales constituting 30 per cent of the VCR market by 1995.[17]

The other view was sceptical. Between 1982 and 1983, VHS sales doubled. So the firms that had committed themselves to VHS had an extremely strong motive to delay the introduction of 8 mm equipment until later in the life cycle of the VHS. JVC's expressed view was that 8 mm was premature, and Panasonic reportedly wanted less 8 mm publicity because of the effect its pre-announcement might have on VHS sales. MITI was rumoured to have told the Japanese firms to delay its introduction.

Although the firms in the VHS camp may have wanted to delay the introduction of the 8 mm standard, those in the Betamax camp (and potential newcomers to the industry) had every incentive to introduce 8 mm as soon as possible. This would present the VHS group members with a difficult choice. If they followed the 8 mm, they would help establish its pre-eminence and cut their own VHS sales. If they did not, they risked falling irretrievably behind the technology's evolution.

What no one knew was the extent to which 8 mm and VHS (and Betamax as well) would compete in the same or in different market niches. One possibility was that the 8 mm would not replace any other format (unless Sony dropped the Betamax in lieu of 8 mm) because it would have overwhelming appeal only to consumers interested in videography. Consumers interested in time-shifting or viewing pre-recorded films would continue to buy and use VHS due to its large installed base of software, lower price, and because VHS had a longer playing duration. (The picture quality of the two alternatives was approximately the same.)

The other possibility was that consumers would accept only one device—the one that best met the composite of their needs. In this case, 8 mm and VHS would be in direct competition.

The camcorder standards conflict

Kodak was the first to introduce an 8 mm line—called *Kodavision*—which appeared in 1984. (Matsushita made the hardware for Kodak.) Thus, there were three different and incompatible camcorders on the market: the 8 mm and the half-inch VHS and the Betamax models. The next three firms into the US market with 8 mm lines were Polaroid, GE, and RCA.

Sony introduced an 8 mm VCR in January 1985 and a camcorder—the Sony *Handycam*—in March. The Handycam had a two-hour recording time (or four hours at half-speed) and weighed only about 2 lb (less than 1 kg), which was less than half the weight of the VHS camcorders. Recordings could be viewed through the camera viewfinder, directly on a TV by cabling the camcorder to the TV, or indirectly by transcribing the 8 mm tape on to a VHS-format tape to be shown on a VHS VCR. (Transcribing, the most popular method, could be done just by cabling the camcorder and the VCR together.

Sony spent more than $10 million promoting its camcorder. Its advertising stressed 8 mm as a new technology to replace both VHS and Betamax (even though Sony did not withdraw Betamax from sale). Sony also reached an agreement in 1986 with Paramount Pictures under which Paramount would release pre-recorded programmes in 8 mm.

Matsushita, JVC, and Hitachi did not market 8 mm lines, but Matsushita did manufacture 8 mm hardware for Kodak, Philips, and GE (for whom it also made VHS VCRs). These OEM contracts were signed before the VHS became dominant in VCRs, so that Matsushita did not have the recourse of boycotting the 8 mm standard entirely. Hitachi manufactured 8 mm hardware for RCA. Only Sanyo made an 8 mm for sale in the United States under its own name.

With the 8 mm, Sony negotiated widely with others, including Aiwa, Kyocera, and Fuji, to manufacture the equipment, and Sony stated that it would make equipment for sale under other brand names.

The VHS-C standard

Early in 1986, JVC counterattacked. It introduced a miniature VHS standard and a camcorder with a cassette that could be played in a standard VHS VCR with an adaptor packaged with the camcorder. The standard was called the *VHS-C* (C for 'compact'). JVC's advertising campaign claimed that 'You don't need some unfamiliar format to get a light camcorder.' This made four incompatible camcorder standards,

8 mm, Betamax, VHS, and VHS-C, with the last two rendered compatible with an adaptor.

The VHS-C cassette was one-third the size of the standard VHS cassette (i.e. slightly larger than the 8 mm) and had a tape capacity of 20 minutes. In April 1986, six firms that were party to the 8 mm agreement—Matsushita, Mitsubishi, JVC, Toshiba, Hitachi, and Sharp—announced that they would adopt the VHS-C (and by implication abandon 8 mm). The same year, RCA adopted VHS-C. Sony alleged that JVC threatened that any firm that adopted 8 mm would be denied a VHS licence, but the charge was never sustained.

Unlike the 8 mm, the VHS-C standard was clearly intended only to solve the portability problem for the videography market. It was not suitable for time-shifting, and there were no pre-recorded tapes. Its picture quality was inferior to the 8 mm's as well. But the VHS-C was perfect for VHS owners who had only casual interest in videography.

Sales of camcorders rose to $400 million in 1985. By 1986, camcorders had become the fastest growing segment of the American consumer electronics industry and sold 1.1 million units for factory revenues of $1100 million. A sales increase of 50 per cent was projected for 1987.

The VHS-C started to outsell the 8 mm for the first time in early 1987, and some analysts predicted that the trend would progressively shift in favour of the VHS-C.[18] But in 1988, the Sony 8 mm camcorder picked up momentum. In that year, Sony sold 1.8 million units and had 50 per cent of the European, 30 per cent of the Japanese, and 20 per cent of the US markets. Part of the improved sales came from slowly rising software availability. In Japan, there were about 500 titles available, the US market had about 250, and in Europe there were 800 titles available. By the end of the decade, the number of titles available in the United States had risen to between 800 and 1000.

The importance of software was a lesson that Sony learnt with the Betamax experience, and it took steps to strengthen its position in the software market in the later 1980s. In 1987, Sony bought CBS Records, which offered music titles and a distribution network that could be useful for video software. In 1989, the company bought Columbia Pictures, giving it access to the 2700 movie titles in Columbia's library.

The end of Betamax

In January 1988, Sony announced that it would begin to sell VHS VCRs. Although Sony allegedly still made a profit on Betamax, it constituted only 20 million of the 170 million VTRs in use world-wide (a 12 per cent market share), and Sony ranked fourteenth among VCR makers. In sales, VHS had 95 per cent of the world market. Sony contended that by offering both VHS (made by Hitachi) and the high end of the Betamax line, which had superior picture and audio quality, it could help sell 8 mm camcorders. Home movies made with the camcorder could be edited by dubbing the camcorder tape on to a regular (VHS or Betamax) VCR tape. Although Sony claimed that it would not abandon the Betamax line or its customers, the announcement was widely interpreted as Sony's final surrender to a superior standard.

B ANALYSIS

Analysis of the period before Betamax and VHS

The first stage of development of the industry was marked by competition between different basic technologies, all of which proved unsatisfactory for a mass consumer market. The main reasons why the mass market proved so elusive were that the equipment was too primitive for a non-technical user and because none of the competing technologies allowed sales prices low enough for a household market. The first stage concluded with the final dominance of magnetic tape recording technology over other alternatives, and with products that for the first time had the functionality, quality, and price to appeal to a mass market. So the second stage opened with a single preferred technology—magnetic tape—but with two competing and incompatible standards. The second stage ended with the dominance of one of them.

Without a mass consumer market, many of the questions central to the strategic use of standards were not relevant. Producers and distributors of complementary products were unimportant. There were no problems of installed bases compatible with one or another standard. Conversion between different standards, to the extent it was necessary, was relatively easy since users were technically sophisticated.[19]

The story of the first stage of the industry's history—the period from Ampex's first model in 1956 to the introductions of Betamax and VHS—does raise some important questions, however. Among them are the following.

1. What role, if any, might standards have played up to the point at which the mass market for VCRs developed?

2. Would an earlier agreement on a standard have been possible and desirable? More generally, when in the evolution of a technology does standardization become feasible and efficient?

3. Did Ampex, the early leader in the market, fail because its strategy *vis-à-vis* standards was flawed?

In the 1950s, the equipment—at prices initially around $50 000—was only suitable for the professional market. Professional users, with the exception of broadcasters, only cared that their equipment was internally standardized. That is, they needed to be able to record, play back, and re-transmit on different pieces of hardware within their own establishments, but they had little reason to seek a common standard for all users. This modest degree of standardization is analogous to what Eli Whitney first achieved in the manufacture and assembly of firearms, but we saw that even this was not achieved with the earliest models of video recorder. This segment of the professional market developed to modest size in the 1960s and then grew significantly in the 1970s when the U-Matic standard was eventually set.

The broadcasters needed interchangeability of tapes between stations and networks. Ampex's tape format was a *de facto* standard in this segment and accounted for the company's near-monopoly.

On the supply side, the producer benefits of standardization were also still far off. The volumes of each vintage of technology were much too small to yield significant economies of scale or experience. In part, this was because the professional market was inherently small and in part it was because the technology evolved so quickly that product life cycles were too short to build volume production.

So in the earliest years of video recorders, standardization between firms was of little value to either users or producers. What is more, standardization could probably not have been achieved even if it had been desired. The many preconditions for standardization would not be met for another decade.

The first precondition for any significant degree of standardization is technological stability. Yet even as late as the end of the 1960s, there were basic technological choices still to be made. Choices of magnetic or non-magnetic tape, of specific magnetic tape recording technologies, of tapes or discs, etc., all predate relatively trivial choices like tape width and cassette size, which themselves were to prove difficult to resolve. It is interesting to observe that even within Ampex, rival technologies were fully developed and that the company actually introduced two different and incompatible products (the VR-303 and VR-3000) that were in direct competition. It is true that 'standards' were repeatedly proclaimed, but often after only a prototype of the equipment had been built.

Although there was a profusion of different technologies and standards in video recording in the 1960s, it is not the number of alternatives that is really important. In audio recording, for example, there has long been a variety of standards on the market simultaneously—record players of different speeds, reel-to-reel tapes, and tape cassettes. Each has achieved reasonable market penetration. But what distinguished this early period in video recording is that none of the technologies had matured to the point at which they could satisfy mass market requirements. Comparing what technology was able to offer in the early 1960s with 1975, we see tape recording densities improved by a factor of more than ten, weight reduced by more than 70 per cent, and costs cut by nearly 90 per cent. Without that maturation, a mass market product and a stable standard were impossible.

The difficulty of achieving standardization so early in the industry's development was due to more than just technological immaturity, however. It was also due to market immaturity. Interestingly, a fairly accurate view of what the mass consumer market would eventually look like dates to the very beginnings of the industry. In the 1950s, one could find descriptions of a future that entailed widespread household ownership of VCRs, of retail and rental outlets for pre-recorded films, and of hand-held cameras that could record for playback on a television.

The technological developments that would have to be made before that future became reality were probably understood. But it seems in retrospect that few understood the nature of consumers' preferences and how those preferences related to the question of standards. For example, as it was not until 1968 that Ampex first realized that there were some distinctly different potential market segments, and that these different segments would put a different value on standards. But Ampex had no idea whether consumers' use of VTRs would first coalesce around playback of pre-recorded tapes, time-shifting of TV programmes, or home movies. In fact, this was unknown even on the introductions of Betamax and VHS. In the end, it only became known when consumers began to experiment with the equipment and to understand its potential.

The problems that an immature market cause standardization often exceed those caused by an immature technology. And they are equally often underestimated despite their critical importance to standardization decisions. In characteristic 'chicken and egg' fashion, for example, the market could not develop as long as consumers neither understood what to do with a VTR nor how to keep one from breaking down. But a broad-based standard is a precondition for building the stocks of software and the distribution channels necessary to teach consumers about VTRs. Yet there could be no broad-based standard until the market developed. It is important to understand how Ampex attempted to get around this problem.

We have seen and will see a number of cases where one of the most difficult questions to answer concerning standards is whether two market segments are sufficiently differentiated that they can sustain incompatible standards. For example, Apple successfully differentiated a relatively homogeneous microcomputer market so that its standards survived with IBM's despite powerful economic forces pushing the industry towards just one standard. Sony, by contrast, was unable to differentiate the VCR market to save Betamax.

In the case of Ampex's VR-7000, we have the opposite question. How similar must two market segments be to accept just one standard? After Ampex's experience with two incompatible products in the same market (the VR-303 and the VR-3000), it next tried to sell one single standard (albeit one that could be altered by writing at full or half-speed) to both the professional market and the mass market. Ampex's hope was that it could lift the mass market standard off the established professional standard.

Ampex's one-inch magnetic tape standard was in competition with an assortment of half-inch standards offered by Japanese firms. The Ampex technology was expensive, high quality, and compatible across its product lines from the low end all the way to broadcasting. The Japanese half-inch models were all incompatible with each other, but for the mass market, each had the advantage of simplicity, lower cost, and reliability. So Ampex was in essence offering the mass market a product that was not ideally suited to it but that Ampex hoped would have the offsetting advantage of standardization with professional machines. Unfortunately, household users had no reason to value standardization with the professionals' machines. There were no network economies on the demand side that linked the two markets. Nor were there significant production economies of scale or scope that would translate into lower prices given the small size of the professional equipment market and Ampex's general neglect (compared with the Japanese) of manufacturing capability.

These early mistakes that Ampex made regarding standards were not to be repeated with Instavideo. Since Ampex was not a consumer goods company and had no marketing agreement with one, it needed to introduce a product that could stand alone with few complementary products and little support from the distribution channels. This would be the best way to get around the chicken and egg problem. The instantaneous response market was ideally suited since consumer network economies would be small and incompatibility between Instavideo and other systems would matter relatively little.

Ampex's position was thus in sharp distinction to that of RCA and CBS. Whereas Ampex needed a stand-alone device that would minimize the company's weaknesses in software and distribution, RCA and CBS wanted to sell systems of hardware and software that would exploit their strengths in consumer retailing and in the production of the software. It is natural that RCA and CBS targeted their products on the playback of pre-recorded tapes. (They intended to create chickens and eggs simultaneously!)

Although these respective strategies seem reasonable, each failed. Ampex's failure was not due to any flaw in its strategy *vis-à-vis* standards, however. Ampex had the hardware, the technological skills, the market analysis, and a leadership position. Furthermore, to target the instantaneous response market was appropriate to developing the nascent mass market that could most easily start with that use and then evolve over time into play of pre-recorded tapes. Unfortunately, Ampex did not have the necessary production expertise or, in the end, the financial resources, so that it was unable to translate its strengths into products that were defendable in the long term.

RCA and CBS had both the production expertise and the financial resources, but their strategies, although natural given the companies' strengths, were inappropriate to developing a standard. Wholly apart from the problem of introducing two competing and incompatible standards, the firms erred in thinking that the mass market would develop around playback-only hardware. As we will see later, the VCR market would have to start growing with stand-alone use before pre-recorded material would ever become sufficiently abundant in retail and rental establishments to develop that market use. And by the time pre-recorded material was abundant, the demand for time-shift TV recording would be so well established that consumers would never accept a device specialized for playback-only.

Would earlier agreement on standards have been desirable? The case suggests that the incompatibilities that existed until the mid-1970s were a necessary consequence of the important process of exploration of technological alternatives. Many different technologies and standards had to be tried before the first successful products appeared, and none of those demonstrated at the various trade shows or conferences at the end of the 1960s and the beginning of the 1970s was to survive. (The U-Matic did, but it was targeted at a different market.) We saw that the same companies frequently changed their standards. For example, Philips' V-2000 was not compatible with its earlier models. VHS was incompatible with the Matsushita model introduced only two years earlier. Ampex introduced several models, including the simultaneous introductions of two that were incompatible.

Only by the mid-1970s were the technological alternatives all tried and tested. Only then was the technology ready for the introductions of Betamax and VHS. There was still market uncertainty, however, and as we will see, Sony and JVC had different expectations of what consumers would use VCRs for.

In conclusion, it is difficult to believe that industry standarization on one technology in the late 1960s or early 1970s would have been desirable. To quote the editorial director of *Television Digest*, 'If we had only one standard, it would probably be one of the early ones that was lousy'.[20] This view was expressed as well by some participants at the ITA conference, and one reason for the failure to find a common standard at that conference was surely the large number of technologies that had still not been sorted through.

Although incompatibility was the necessary price to pay for technological experimentation up to the mid-1970s, it is less clear that the incompatibility between Betamax and VHS was equally desirable. That issue will be addressed in the next section.

From Betamax and VHS to VHS alone

With the introductions of Betamax and VHS in 1975 and 1976, the first stage of the development of the video recording industry ended and the second started. The first stage ended with the dominance of magnetic tape recording technology over all other alternatives. The second stage ended with the dominance of one magnetic tape standard—VHS.

To understand this episode in the VCR story, one must try to answer two questions. First, why did two similar but incompatible standards appear on the market at approximately the same time? This contradicts what the theoretical literature discussed in Chapter 1 would have one expect. Would it not have been better for Sony and JVC to agree on a single standard? Second, why did JVC's VHS standard ultimately prevail over Sony's Betamax?

The competitive setting in the mid-1970s resembled a game called 'the battle of the sexes'.[21] JVC preferred VHS while Sony preferred Betamax.[22] However (to fit the game's assumptions), both would be better off with a single common standard (either VHS or Beta) because incompatible standards would inhibit market growth. In game theory terms, either all-VHS or all-Beta are asymmetric equilibria whereas both standards coexisting is not an equilibrium.

In this game, each firm has a motive to be the first to present the other with an inflexible position. If, for example, Sony were to commit itself in an absolutely credible way to Betamax irrespective of JVC's plans, then it would be best for JVC to go along with Betamax and abandon VHS. Since Sony had invested in the tooling and a greenfield production facility and was in the lead when the negotiations between the companies were undertaken, it was positioned to make the irrevocable launch commitment. Why, then, did the others refuse to take Beta once it had been launched?

What makes the introductions of both Betamax and VHS especially surprising is that MITI would surely have tried to arrange some means whereby the firm that surrendered its standard in favour of the other would be compensated. The possibility of side payments is normally ruled out of the battle of the sexes game, but with relevance to this case, side payments should only strengthen the motive of the firms to agree on a common standard. Side payments allow the efficient solution—a common standard—that can make all parties to the game better off.

The explanation of the seemingly self-destructive behaviour—especially on the part of JVC and Matsushita which were followers chronologically—is found in differences between the battle of the sexes and the reality of the competitive situation facing these two firms. JVC and Matsushita obviously believed they were better off with the two standards on the market than converting to Betamax even though it was available royalty-free. Why would they have thought so? The changeover to Betamax would surely have been costly both in manufacturing and in engineering terms. Furthermore, they might have feared that a late start would leave them irrevocably behind as the technology

84

evolved. (Although this may have been a reasonable fear at the time, neither VHS nor Beta ever changed significantly, and there is no evidence that the various licensees of each were ever at a technological disadvantage.) Still, some compensation scheme should have been feasible to offset these concerns.

It is possible also that JVC and Matsushita expected VHS eventually to displace Betamax given its longer playing time. That is, Sony and JVC/Matsushita may have had different visions of the pay-off matrix. In retrospect, JVC and Matsushita were correct, of course, but their future success would not have been obvious at the time. The big advantage that VHS had in recording time, which proved critically important for the success of VHS, was not fully realized until it was extended to four hours to satisfy RCA in 1977.

There might have been 'irrational' reasons for the decision to pursue VHS. Perhaps the firms felt that they could not afford to lose the millions of dollars they had already invested in their proprietary technology. This is not a relevant consideration, of course, since those dollars were sunk once spent. None the less, managers often fail to understand the concept of a sunk cost. The 'not invented here' mentality might explain why a JVC engineer would eschew Betamax,[23] and for senior management to impose Betamax on the company might harm the morale of the source of JVC's economic rents—its development engineers.

In any case, a few observations are important. One is that management must appreciate the strategic significance of decisions on standards early in the design cycle. Even though such decisions are often regarded as technical ones to be delegated to technical people, they can quickly create undesired commitments.

Another observation is that although a first-mover advantage might seem to be decisive in a competitive setting such as existed here (especially given Sony's irrevocable commitment to Betamax), it was not. JVC introduced a second incompatible standard late and then prevailed. The case suggests that competitive strategy and/or technological capability can overcome a late start.

A final point is that collective efforts at setting industry-wide standards must generally start at the pre-competitive stage and before narrow vested interests for a particular standard take hold. Once significant research and development is undertaken, prototypes built, public announcements made, and personal careers implicated, it is often too late to negotiate. It is significant that in this case, much of the early

85

development was done in secret. In fact, JVC only revealed its VHS equipment to Matsushita—its parent—when Betamax was launched.

Although we may not know exactly why JVC and Matsushita chose to introduce VHS once Betamax was a *fait accompli*, they were clearly right to have done so considering their eventual commercial success. But that does not mean that it was socially desirable that two incompatible standards based on the same technology coexisted on the market for more than ten years. If we assume that MITI had the power to compel an agreement (and that it was intent on serving consumers' interests), should it have forced one standard on the industry back in 1976?

A comparison of inter-standards competition (i.e. competition between Beta and VHS) with intra-standard competition (i.e. competition between licensees of the same standard, be it Beta or VHS) is complicated even if one assumes the two standards are homogeneous. Inter-standards competition entails all the costs of incompatibility that have been discussed previously. These include the extra production and distribution costs of software compatible with different standards, consumer confusion over different standards and hesitancy to commit to one or the other with no assurance of its continuity, an inability of one consumer to share tapes with others, etc. There may have been unnecessary supply-side costs, too, in both research and development and manufacturing.

Yet consumers could none the less benefit from inter-standards competition in a number of ways. First, price competition was obviously keen between the Betamax and the VHS coalitions, and we saw repeated episodes of price cutting. Second, there was competition between the two standards to add differentiating features. Finally, one way to win the inter-standard competition was to license other producers. This would depress royalties (JVC's royalty on VHS was only 3.5 per cent of sales revenues) and intensify price and non-price competition between the different licensees of the same standard. With the same technology, these were the sole bases for gaining a competitive advantage. The induced intra-standards competition clearly improved the competitive structure of the industry.

Why did VHS eventually displace Betamax? There are two points that are central to answering this question. First, two undifferentiated but incompatible standards in the market produced an unstable situation. Natural economic forces principally on the demand side of the market drove convergence towards just one. Second, the strategy that

JVC and Matsushita used to expand the network of VHS was superior to Sony's strategy.

If the two standards were very clearly differentiated, they might have been able to coexist. Sony tried to differentiate Betamax and thus to stop the market shift towards VHS. There were, of course, some basic differences between the two technologies. VHS had longer play time and was less expensive than Betamax. But the consensus of opinion was that Betamax had superior picture and audio quality (although this superiority diminished as VHS improved). Unfortunately for Sony, play time was the only difference that was really important to consumers. To quote a retailer at the time, 'Except for the difference in playing time, and the fact that their cassettes are not interchangeable, the two systems are identical for all practical purposes. We advise our customers to buy the VCRs that offer the longest playing time.'[24] Thus, technology differences, albeit modest, provided an unambiguous advantage for VHS rather than a segmented market. This advantage persisted until Betamax's play time was improved.

Sony continued to try to differentiate Betamax from VHS by adding peripheral features. Unfortunately, there was nothing intrinsic to Betamax that defied duplication by VHS. For example, Sony added stereophonic sound but Panasonic (a VHS supplier) soon followed. It introduced Betamovie—a one-piece camera-recorder using the Betamax format. This too was copied. (Of course, imitation also worked to Sony's advantage. It extended the Betamax play time to match that of VHS, and it imitated features like remote control that VHS was the first to embody.)

With strong economic forces pushing the market to a single standard and no significant technological differentiation to resist those forces, the market was destined to converge from two standards to one. Why was the convergence to VHS rather than to Betamax?

Sony had an 18-month headstart—a considerable first-mover advantage that in the arena of standards competition can often be decisive. But there were some advantages in being a follower that JVC and Matsushita exploited. Since VCRs were early in their life cycle, it was important to advertise the generic product. As one senior marketing manager said of plans to promote Betamax, 'Our first promotions will concentrate on why you should invest $1300 in a recording device'.[25] Sony's advertising to promote the use of VCRs, which amounted to $300–$400 per machine by late 1977, was free advertising for JVC. Yet before 'Betamax' became synonymous with 'VCR', Matsushita and the other VHS producers were able to emphasize VHS's advantages over Betamax.

The longer recording time of VHS was a major competitive advantage, as was noted above. It was especially important to RCA who foresaw the demand to record long televized events like sports. The fact that Matsushita doubled the VHS recording time for RCA is a testament to the company's and to the product's flexibility. VHS proved ideal for recording long TV 'specials' because its cassette capacity had been planned for lengthy pre-recorded material. Recorded TV specials were often kept for repeated viewing and shared between households as were professionally pre-recorded tapes, so that in some ways, this use was similar to that of VHS's initial target market. Sony, by contrast, had targeted Betamax for time-shift TV viewing only, and it did not envision programmes of the length that RCA foresaw. Sony managed to extend Betamax's recording time (and even resorted to pre-announcements of the improvements),[26] but VHS held the advantage when it was critical.

Another advantage VHS held was a lower price, at least early in the battle. Sony's 'skimming' strategy—a strategy of premium pricing that was common in much of its product line—was not suited to developing a bandwagon for Betamax. Even if the market for Betamax were price inelastic, so that a price increase would increase revenues, the lower market share that a higher price implies would in the longer run shift more consumers—and thus software producers—to VHS. Sony repeatedly cut its price, but the cuts were matched by VHS. Matsushita's superior strategy of price leadership was made possible by its lower production costs, which in turn were due to the company's larger volumes and its historic production expertise.[27]

Next, JVC and Matsushita licensed the VHS technology liberally, and in so doing they built an exceptionally strong marketing position. VHS equipment was produced by numerous Japanese firms and was re-labelled and resold by many of their American and European subsidiaries as well as independent companies like Magnavox, Sylvania, RCA, and Philips. Sony's licensing policy, by contrast, was more restricted and appears to be a defensive move rather than a first preference.

Finally, Sony's position with the smaller of the two standards networks—for reasons noted above—proved a disaster when the market for viewing pre-recorded tapes developed. Sony had not expected such high use of pre-recorded material, and it had not developed a strategy for it. Sony had no links with software copyright holders and no control over the software distribution channels, so there was nothing it could do to counter the larger VHS market share. The result was that there were fewer Betamax tapes produced and stocked in the retail outlets and rental shops.

In the end, increases in the VHS market share were self-reinforcing as more sales meant lower production costs, lower prices, more sales, more rental tapes, and still more sales. Some companies initially producing or marketing Betamax like Toshiba and Zenith switched to VHS. Finally, Sony did too.

Videotapes and videodiscs or videotapes only?

Although Betamax and VHS were little-differentiated products competing in a natural monopoly setting, the case of VCRs versus videodiscs is very different. Here we see two clearly differentiated technologies and associated standards in quasi-competition. (This same setting reappeared shortly after in the case of the camcorder.)

The question that faced the industry was whether these two technologies could coexist or whether the VCRs, which could perform all of the functions of the videodiscs and more, would displace the videodiscs. Of course, the setting was complicated by the fact that within both VCRs and videodiscs, there were multiple incompatible standards. In retrospect, it might appear obvious that videodiscs were doomed. But it is worth noting that industry experts at the time feared that videodisc players would cannibalize the market for VCRs, and many urged that the introduction of videodiscs be postponed for that reason.

Two fundamental questions are relevant to analysing the potential for videodiscs. First, how much better (in terms of both quality and price) were the videodiscs and their software than the VCRs for viewing pre-recorded films? Second, in what way would the two market segments—viewing pre-recorded software and time-shift TV viewing—be differentiable?[28]

Regarding the second question, there are two ways in which these markets might segment—ways that are described here in their extremes. One is if each consumer preferred either to watch pre-recorded tapes or else to record TV programmes, but no consumer cared to do both. We can define this as the case of 'specialized' consumer preferences. In this case, videodiscs should find a ready market presuming that they were superior to VCRs for watching pre-recorded tapes (again in terms of quality and price). The market shares of videodiscs and VCRs should be the same as the shares of consumers interested in the use to which each product was focused.

If, by contrast, every single consumer wanted to view pre-recorded films and also to record TV programmes, that is consumers had generalized or 'portfolio' preferences, then videodiscs would have a harder time establishing themselves. Even if they were superior to VCRs for viewing pre-recorded films, videodiscs would still have to compete with VCRs in that use since many households would find it uneconomical to have both a general-purpose VCR and a special-purpose videodisc player. One would expect that the market share of the VCRs would be higher than the per cent of usage represented by time-shifting. How much higher would depend, among other things, on the cost of the equipment and the extent of the videodiscs' superiority in viewing pre-recorded material.

The implications of how consumer preferences split between specialized and generalized are considerable. For time-shifting (and for videography), a universal standard is relatively unimportant. There may be economies of scale and experience in production although the multiple licensees in the VCR industry would seem to deny it. In any case, there are few consumer benefits that arise directly from standardization. All that matters is that each user has a compatible videorecorder and TV (and possibly camera). The big economies of a universal standard only appear with pre-recorded software. Thus, under the most optimistic scenario for videodiscs—a world of specialized preferences—their success would be particularly sensitive to the existence of a universal videodisc standard. The fact that there were incompatible videodisc standards on the market must have seriously hindered its development and may have done more to kill the videodisc than any limitation of the technology *per se*.

There is evidence that many consumers did have specialized preferences and that these preferences varied by country. The play of pre-recorded tapes constituted 75 per cent of recorder usage in Europe and 50 per cent in the United States (but only 5 per cent in Japan). In West Germany, for example, with only two national broadcast networks and no cable or satellite video transmission, time-shifting was of little use, and West Germany was one of the largest software markets in the world. Cassette rentals there in 1983 amounted to $200 million. So all things being equal, one would expect that the videodisc would find a better market in Europe than in the United States or Japan. It is unsurprising that the product was not a Japanese development.

This analysis suggests a wisdom to Philips' strategy of offering two distinct products with a focus on the European market. One was the V-

2000 VCR and the other was laservideo. As is often the case, however, problems in execution can disguise possible wisdom in conceptualization. Philips' V-2000 was too late to enter too small a market, it was technologically overdone and thus expensive and unreliable, and it was poorly marketed. And laservideo (and other VCRs used with pre-recorded tapes) naturally would cannibalize some of its sales.

One can never know whether the laservideo concept might have succeeded under better circumstances. Laservideo did have a potential market given European viewing preferences. Both the hardware and the software were cheaper than that for the VCR, and its picture quality was superior. It would seem, however, that these advantages were insufficient to sustain videodisc even in a market setting most advantageous to it. The film production cost and price differential might have been decisive if consumers chose to invest in their own film libraries. But if they chose to rent films instead, as was the case, then it would be much less important.

Videodiscs eventually failed because: (a) many consumers had generalized preferences; (b) videodiscs were only moderately better in their specialized function than were the more general purpose VCRs; (c) they were expensive;[29] (d) the proliferation of videodisc standards inhibited production of the required software; and (e) by the time videodiscs appeared, standards in the VCR industry were finally converging. So software was prepared for the VCRs instead of the videodiscs.

Camcorders: 8 mm or VHS-C?

Much of the story of camcorders is similar to the story of videodiscs. We again have a question of whether alternative technologies and standards are sufficiently differentiated to coexist. And whether consumers have specialized or generalized preferences for pre-recorded tape viewing, time-shifting, and videography again prove important. But there is one major difference. The 8 mm standard is not inherently specialized. Unlike, videodiscs, 8 mm can perform all the functions of the half-inch VCRs.

The story of competition in camcorders is also similar in some ways to the story of Betamax versus VHS. Again we have competition between different standards for VCRs. But there is again a major difference with respect to the earlier episode. For the first time, problems arise from the installed base of investments that the mass consumer market made in earlier technologies.

Sony faced a number of strategic questions concerning how to develop

91

the 8 mm standard. It could either promote 8 mm as a specialized standard aimed at videography or it could promote it as a replacement for the half-inch standards and a platform for further development of miniature video-recording applications. Our earlier analysis of the industry suggests two generalizations relevant to making this choice. One is that it is generally easier to launch a new standard into a vacuum than it is to displace an existing standard with an installed base. The second is that it is generally easier to launch a new standard into a niche in which its inevitable lack of an existing base of complementary products is least damaging.

Both these generalizations suggest that the 8 mm should first be directed at the videography market. The smaller cassette had the greatest relative advantage there. That is, the existing standards (VHS and Beta) were least appropriate. And videography required no infrastructure of complementary products like pre-recorded tapes. To the extent that some consumers had specialized preferences for videography, 8 mm could establish a beach-head in that market segment from which it could later migrate into the market for viewing pre-recorded tapes as they became available. Sony's acquisitions of CBS Records and Columbia Pictures were clearly intended to provide those tapes.

Another strategic question that Sony must have contemplated was whether to open its 8 mm development to others to get agreement on an industry-wide standard or else to try to develop 8 mm technology alone. This is the same issue of open versus proprietary system standards that is the focus of Chapter 5.

Sony chose to target its product development at videography while at the same time advertising 8 mm as a near-term replacement for all existing VCR formats. In a sense, Sony tried to avoid the first choice noted above. The virtue of this approach was that it might improve 8 mm sales prospects to consumers with generalized preferences. But at the same time, it constituted a much greater threat to the VHS producers—a threat to which they responded.

If Sony did indeed intend 8 mm as a near-term replacement for the existing VCR formats, it made sense for a number of reasons to open the standard to the industry. It would help build support for the standard, and Sony might have hoped that openness would mitigate the opposition of the VHS producers. Furthermore, 8 mm entailed little proprietary technology that could have been used to exclude other firms had they wanted to adopt the standard. Finally, Sony had been

92

chastened by the experience of Betamax and was now much more willing as a general matter to seek industry-wide accords.

The 8 mm agreement reached in 1983 meant in principle that for the first time, there would be an industry-wide non-proprietary standard that would ensure that all video recorders would soon be compatible.

The 8 mm agreement was possible because the problems that confounded earlier attempts at industry standardization—for example, the attempts of the ITA in 1971 and 1972—were solved. The market was much more mature on both the demand and supply sides, there was only one basic technology at issue, and there was a small and obvious group of leaders. Furthermore, unlike in the case of Betamax and VHS, the 8 mm standard was non-proprietary, and no firm had an unbeatable lead in developing it.

Unfortunately, when one problem was solved, another appeared. Although the 8 mm technology *per se* was equally available to all, the starting positions of the competitors were not equal because of the success of VHS. So the market again split in two, this time according to whether the firms were or were not part of the VHS camp, that is, whether they had an installed base to protect or not.

There was another and related two-way split of the competitors. This split was between the photographic firms like Kodak, Polaroid, Canon, and Olympus on the one hand and the consumer electronics firms making TVs, VCRs, and audio hi-fi equipment on the other. The former universally endorsed 8 mm both because they had no vested interests in VHS and because their market experience was with videography to which 8 mm was especially well suited. (Kodak and Polaroid were being driven by the obsolescence of their traditional markets to look to new technologies like camcorders.)

Sony may have tried to mitigate industry opposition by promoting 8 mm as an open standard, but the VHS producers still had a strong motive to boycott or in some other way to delay it. To embrace it would cannibalize the still strong VHS sales. But to neglect it would risk falling behind in 8 mm development.

The counterstrategy that JVC chose—to introduce an interim miniature standard compatible with VHS through a converter—is a particularly imaginative one. With VHS-C, JVC managed to undermine the clear advantage that 8 mm had in videography. Although the picture quality of the 8 mm was superior, VHS-C was better for time-shifting since its recording time was longer, and 8 mm had only a small stock of pre-recorded films available (although Sony's ventures with the software companies were threatening). The fact that VHS-C could be used with an existing VHS recorder further lowered its cost to consumers. So the VHS producers could extend the lifetime of VHS and wait until the 8 mm format matured (if it ever did) before being forced into it.

Sony's rebuttal has been to emphasize the potentially superior upgrade path that might be possible with 8 mm. Its major technological advantage was that everything in the camcorder was reduced in size and weight with no design constraints imposed by an existing standard. So it was fundamentally lighter, smaller, and lower cost, and thus would be a better base for the next generation of VCRs than the interim VHS-C.

At the time of this writing, Sony seems to be succeeding brilliantly with its newest camcorder, the CCD-TR55. It has become the industry's best selling product in years, and Canon, Ricoh, and Hitachi have joined the 8 mm bandwagon with their own lightweight camcorders. In fact, there has been industry speculation that this success may be sufficient to lead to the ultimate doom of VHS.[30]

Conclusions

The case of Betamax and VHS is a classic in its portrayal of the dynamics of competition between alternative yet undifferentiated proprietary technological standards. Although starting from behind, VHS has now become established as the dominant VCR standard partly as a result of superior technology but more importantly as a result of Matsushita's superior use of the competitive tools that standardization renders important. These include in particular pricing, distribution, and technology licensing. The competitive battles between different technologies, both before and after the principal one of Betamax and VHS, have illustrated other important phenomena—market differentiation and segmentation, product positioning, open versus proprietary standards, installed bases compatible with one standard or another, the achievement of compatibility with an adaptor as opposed to true standarization, and co-production of complementary products—that appear in other cases in this book and elsewhere and that must be understood if one is to use standarization to gain competitive advantage in the marketplace.

Notes and references
1. In this chapter, a distinction will be drawn between VTRs and VCRs. In the former, the tape is exposed and must be wound on a spool by the user.

In the latter, the tape is housed in a cassette and is automatically wound and rewound on the spools.

2. RCA developed a prototype VTR in 1953, but it was not introduced to the commercial market.

3. Sony built Japan's first audio tape recorder in 1950. Sony left the business to concentrate on the transistor technology that was later to attract Ampex's attention.

4. *Wall Street Journal*, 16 April, 1956, p.16.

5. *New York Times*, 22 April, 1956, p.13.

6. It is surprising that it took Ampex so long to discover its mistake. It may be significant that in the early 1960s, Ampex's VTR business was run by its Professional Products Division rather than by Ampex Audio, Inc., the division most familiar with consumer markets.

7. *Educational Television*, October 1970.

8. *Photographic Trade News*, 1 October, 1970.

9. *Merchandising Week*, 17 May, 1971.

10. *Ibid.*

11. *Ibid.*

12. AVCO dropped out of the industry in 1973 with a loss of $60 million.

13. Ampex continued to earn royalty income from patented technology that was adopted by U-Matic and VHS machines.

14. In December 1976, Quasar (which was owned by Matsushita) started to sell the 'Great Time Machine' in the United States. This VCR was developed from the VX-2000 (and thus was incompatible with all other VCRs).

15. Philips had a cross-licensing agreement with Matsushita dating to the postwar reconstruction period in Japan.

16. Betamax has maintained dominance in a few regional markets. For example, it has 90 per cent of the Mexican market and 70 per cent of the Indonesian. It is also strong in the Middle East and Singapore.

17. Wilkofsy Gruen Associates, New York, 1986.

18. Dean Witter Reynolds, Inc., 1987.

19. This was equally true in the computer industry in its early days.

20. Quoted in *Fortune*, 16 July, 1979.

21. See Luce, D. and H. Raiffa, *Games and Decisions*, Wiley, New York, 1957, pp. 90–4. Note that in the VCR case, the game was played only once so that a mixed strategy was impossible.

22. One might argue that there was a third party present—Matsushita—that, although financially related to JVC, acted independently. For the sake of the argument here, Matsushita will be neglected.

23. Although VHS was based on U-Matic technology originating from Sony.

24. Quoted by *Business Week*, 25 June, 1979.

25. Quoted in *Fortune*, September 1977, p.182.

26. See *Fortune*, September 1977.

27. See Quinn, J. B., Managing innovation, *Harvard Business Review*, May/June 1985.

28. There was also a market segment interested in videography, but it can be neglected here without altering the logic of the analysis or the conclusions that follow.
29. By comparison, audio equipment is cheap enough that households commonly have a phonograph turntable, an audio cassette player, and often a compact disc player as well.
30. See *The Economist*, 30 June, 1990.

4. The automobile industry before 1930

Introduction

The early history of the automobile industry in the United States represents one of the best examples of voluntary and cooperative inter-firm agreements on standards. Although there have been disputes over standards, as the following story will show, the industry is one in which there are many cooperatively set standards that have been extremely important to its development. In fact, the success of this cooperation has afforded an example that many other industries subsequently followed.[1]

How was it possible for the many firms in the early history of this industry to agree on standards? What obstacles were there, if any, to setting standards? What role was played by industry standards-setting bodies? Why are some parts like spark plugs, batteries, and wheel rims standardized but not other parts like bumpers? What is the relationship between standardization, variety, and mass production? And finally, what have been the consequences for the industry of the standardization that has been observed? These are some of the questions that will be addressed in this chapter.

The birth of the industry: 1895–1910

Neither individual nor date marks the origin of the automobile. The particular technical developments that made it possible were the work of many different people in the second half of the nineteenth century. Most of that work, and the creation of the first vehicles that we would now regard as 'cars', took place in Europe. Yet the story of the automobile is not one of its creation, which has bequeathed history little of importance. Rather, the story of the automobile is one of its production. Although few readers would know the names of those who played important roles in creating the automobile, all know Henry Ford and his contribution to its manufacture and to the methods of mass production generally. Furthermore, this story is uniquely American—a story that started just before 1900 and ended the decade before the Second World War when US firms were producing 85 per cent of the

97

Table 4.1 Automobile firms and production: 1900–10

Year	No. of entrants	No. of exits	No. of firms remaining	Production
1900	—	—	—	5000
1901	—	—	—	7000
1902	—	—	12	9000
1903	13	1	24	11 235
1904	12	1	35	22 419
1905	5	2	38	24 550
1906	6	1	43	33 500
1907	1	0	44	43 300
1908	10	2	52	63 500
1909	18	1	69	127 731
1910	1	18	52	181 000

Source: Epstein, R., *The Automobile Industry*, Shaw, Chicago, 1928, pp. 176, 177, 314.

world's cars and when the industry was well on its way towards the structure it sustained until the 1980s.

This story of standards in the automobile industry is also centred on the American industry from about 1895 to 1930. The reason is that standards were not significant to the original creation of the automobile. But as we shall see, they played an extremely important role in its production and in the development of the industry's structure in the United States in this period.

In 1895, four automobiles were built in the United States. Four years later, 2500 cars were made. Yet despite the change in numbers, the method of production was the same. These early automobiles were individually built by mechanics in their garages or shops, and each individual vehicle was unique.

Starting around 1900, however, one could begin to identify standardized 'models' of automobile—those of Stanley, Winton, Pope, Olds, and perhaps half a dozen others. And as the first decade progressed, scores more producers started up in the car business (see Table 4.1). This was easy to do because financing was available (despite the fact that banks would not lend to the fledgling and thus risky industry). Significantly for the story that follows, the early firms only designed and assembled cars. They bought all the parts and materials they used on 30- or 60-day credit from companies in other industries (e.g. foundries, machine shops, and carriage makers), and they sold their finished vehicles for cash either directly to the end customer or to an independent dealer.

As is often the case in the early development of any truly novel product, basic design characteristics took a long time to coalesce. A vintage 1905 car could have an electric, steam, or petrol engine. A petrol powered car could be found with stationary or rotary engine, one to six cylinders, two or four cycles, and air or water cooling. The car could have front or rear engine placement, three or four wheels, and a tiller, bar, or steering wheel. Steering wheels were mostly, but not exclusively, on the right in imitation of European cars. The power train might be gear, chain, or drive shaft, the transmission planetary or sliding gear, there might be two, three, or four speeds forward, and ignition might be by battery or magneto.

This profusion of designs meant that automobile prices were high because of the low volumes in which they were produced. Potential customers were confused by the variety, and many understandably felt it wise to await the disappearance of the poorer concepts. The variety of fuels delayed the development of fuelling stations. Perhaps even more discouraging to the industry's early development was the cost of maintenance and repair. Even as late as 1910, this cost often equalled or exceeded a car's capital and fuel costs. In 1906, the life expectancy of chassis springs was 1200 to 2000 miles. Tyres lasted for only 2000 to 3000 miles. And spare parts were extremely expensive. A Ford car tyre cost $30, and tyres for larger cars cost up to $80. The reason for the high cost was that spares were completely unstandardized and thus produced in low volume at high cost with high distribution costs as well. And skilled mechanics—of which there were few—were unequal to the challenge of the variety of technologies that drove these early cars. A Cadillac advertisement hinted at the seriousness of the problem when it claimed, 'When you buy a Cadillac, you buy a round trip.'[2]

The first car to be produced in quantity over a period of years was the 'Curved-Dash' Oldsmobile. It started in production in 1901 when 600 were made. In the next three years, 2500, 4000, and 5000 were made. But although it was inexpensive, the car lacked the power and the robustness that the Model T later offered, and it cannot be considered a truly standardized and mass produced car in the sense that the Model T proved to be.

By 1910, the profusion of designs had been effectively eliminated. By then, the 'standard' $3000 car was rear wheel driven and petrol powered with a four cylinder, water cooled engine, sliding gear transmission, three speeds forward, and magneto ignition. The 'H'-slot gearstick was almost universally employed, and with wider car bodies, it had moved inside the cab and usually on to the steering column. The steering wheel had moved from the right to the left side of the car to afford better visibility forward when driving on the right-hand side of the road and to allow passengers (especially women) to enter the car from the curb.

The reduction in design variety and a drop in the number of firms around 1910 came about because consumer preferences were focusing on four-cylinder, petrol-engine models. In addition to eliminating producers wedded to abandoned technologies, this preference for relatively large and sophisticated cars meant that successful producers needed considerable design and manufacturing skill. They also required more capital than before. With more expensive jigs, dies, templates, and machinery came the need to reduce the variety of models and increase their production rates to amortize fixed costs.

This growing standardization around fewer basic design alternatives was not due to industry-wide planning. Rather, it was due to the market success of some designs over others. Nevertheless, fewer varieties and higher production volumes afforded producers more efficient production. It also made it easier for a driver accustomed to one car to shift to another and for a mechanic knowledgeable about one model to fix a different one. Still, individual models had more idiosyncrasies than now, and smooth gear changing continued for many years to require familiarity with each individual car model.

The Seldon patent and the ALAM: 1900–11

In 1900, the holders of the basic automobile patent—the Seldon patent—filed their first infringement suit against other car makers. The Seldon patent had been issued to George B. Seldon in 1895 and, depending upon one's interpretation of it, covered anything from one specific type of petrol engine to virtually all internal combustion engine automobiles.[3] Seldon never exploited his patent—in fact, he never produced a single car that used it—and in 1899, he sold it to a group of businessmen who had recently formed the Electric Vehicle Company.[4] It was they who tried to exploit the patent by requiring all makers of petrol engine cars to take out licences.

In the settlement of the suit in 1903, the defendants (who were then followed by most other unlicensed car makers) accepted the validity of the patent and agreed to pay a royalty of 1.25 per cent of the retail prices of their cars.[5] But, in addition, they negotiated with the Seldon patent holders the formation of the Association of Licensed Automobile

Manufacturers (ALAM). The ALAM, the first of a number of important industry associations, would receive 40 per cent of the patent royalties, which it would use for the benefit of the entire industry. The ALAM would also have the authority to decide to whom to grant a licence. With its expansive interpretation of the patent's coverage and the growing industry reliance on petrol engines, this was tantamount to the ALAM determining admission to the industry.

The ALAM chose to execute the two tasks of its charter—benefiting the industry and determining entry to it—by the use of industry standards, and it was thus the first automobile industry association to concern itself with standards. In executing these two tasks, however, the ALAM became involved with two quite different types of standards.

Starting around 1906, the ALAM made the first industry attempt to set inter-company technical standards for purchased parts and materials. The attempt—only partly successful—was intended to reduce the tremendous number of nearly identical components by agreeing on a few standard dimensions and specifications for parts like spark plugs, wheel rims, screw threads, and types of purchased steel.[6]

In addition to setting technical standards, however, the ALAM also tried to set automobile 'quality' standards for the industry. The ostensible intent was to protect investors and consumers from 'fly-by-night' firms. Manufacturers who failed to meet these quality standards would not be granted the licences necessary to build cars.

There is some difference of historical opinion about the true intentions underlying these quality standards. Some believe that the intent of the standards was to monopolize the industry by excluding competitors. Others take a more sympathetic view of the ALAM.[7] The latter is at least plausible because there were in fact many fraudulent firms, and because although the organization did deny licences to legitimate firms, it never attempted to restrict the output of its many licence holders. In any case, the ALAM never succeeded in creating a monopoly irrespective of its objective.

The year 1903 celebrated not only the formation of the ALAM but also the founding of the Ford Motor Company. When Henry Ford enquired about his prospects of getting a licence, he was told that because he was only starting, he had not demonstrated that he could meet the ALAM's standards. Expecting that he would be denied a licence, Ford chose to ignore the patent.

The ALAM sued Ford for patent infringement in 1903. But despite the widespread industry respect for the patent's validity, that validity

101

had never been tested in court. Ford challenged it and was joined in its fight by 20 other unlicensed manufacturers who in 1905 formed the American Motor Car Manufacturers' Association (the AMCMA) as a counterpart to the ALAM.

When the ALAM's case against Ford and its allies came to court, the ALAM had 80 members and the AMCMA around 40 with perhaps an additional 100 firms uncommitted to either association. Ford was defeated in district court in 1909, and the defeat caused the collapse of the AMCMA. Ford appealed against the decision, however, and the legal battle was resumed.[8]

In 1911, the Circuit Court of Appeals finally ended the battle by ruling that although the Seldon patent was valid, its coverage was narrow and applied only to one very specific type of engine—not that which in various forms was used by Ford and most other non-licensed producers.[9] With its court defeat, the ALAM disappeared.

Regardless of their intentions, the Seldon patent holders ultimately proved impotent to control the industry. Even when its power was widely accepted, the ALAM never really succeeded in restraining entry into the rapidly growing industry. Many firms in addition to Ford started to build cars without a licence. From a peak in 1905 when the ALAM had 75 per cent of the industry's firms as members, its membership fell to a low of about 45 per cent in 1908. More companies were producing cars at the end of the first decade of the twentieth century, when the patent loomed most ominously over the industry, than at any time before or for a few years after. Perhaps the major damage that the licensing litigation caused was to distract attention and money from the more important challenge of setting variety-reducing standards.

The historical importance of the Seldon patent and the ALAM goes beyond what has been described, however. More significantly, this decade of conflict convinced the industry that patent disputes were collectively damaging. So in 1915, the industry adopted an agreement on mutual cross-licensing of patents whereby participating companies would have royalty-free access to a patent one year after its issue. The cross-licensing system was managed by the successor to the ALAM— the National Automobile Chamber of Commerce (NACC).[10] By the mid-1920s, the NACC managed about 300 patents for various parts of a car.

The cross-licensing agreement was not universal. Patents embodying major technological innovations were to be restricted.[11] The agreement did not apply to parts manufacturers, either. And some car makers did not join. Ford never joined although it did offer its patents to others and freely took theirs in return. None the less, the system worked until it was revised in 1925 to exclude all new patents.

Small firms, large firms, and industry standardization: 1910–20

When the ALAM disappeared in 1910, its mechanical branch, which was responsible for setting technical standards, was absorbed by the Society of Automobile Engineers (SAE).[12] The SAE, which had been formed in 1905, took up the task of negotiating standards agreements for components, publishing those standards, and distributing them throughout the industry. This organization differed from the NACC— the ALAM's successor—in that it was a professional engineering society whose members were individuals rather than firms. When first set up, the standards committee of the SAE had 96 members.

Whereas the technical standards work of the ALAM was relatively uncontroversial, that of the SAE in the second decade of the century divided the industry. The reason for the different experiences of the two standards bodies was that individual firms were beginning to emerge from the early competition with significant market shares. For the first time, the industry could be segregated into small and large firms (especially Ford and General Motors (GM)), and standards divided their interests. For reasons that we will see, the small firms wanted much more industry standardization than did the large firms.

Ford's Model T first went on sale in 1908, and by 1910 it had begun to prove a spectacular success. General Motors was formed in 1908, and by 1910 it had consolidated 20 small firms (including Buick, Cadillac, and Oldsmobile).[13] Together, the two companies comprised 30 per cent of the entire American market. Ford had about 10 per cent and GM 20 per cent.

At this time, the small firms differed from the large firms in two ways. Obviously, they produced fewer cars per year, but they were also less integrated upstream into components manufacturing. They continued in the original tradition of the industry to assemble cars from purchased parts. By contrast, by 1915, most of the large firms were making their own engines, transmissions, axles, etc.

Upstream integration in the car industry became economic for the large firms because they had sufficiently high production rates. In 1903, the *median* output of a car producer was 200 cars. In 1909, this rose to 500. In 1916, it was still only 2000. This was far too low to permit integration into making parts. But the *mean* outputs in those years was 470, 1850, and slightly over 20 000 respectively. Comparison of medians and means shows the process of concentration that was occurring. The largest producer in 1903 made fewer than 4000 cars. By 1908, that figure had more than doubled, and it more than doubled again between 1908 and 1909. In 1913, the five largest firms comprised 46 per cent of the industry's output. In 1916, they comprised over 65 per cent.

With few car parts subject to industry-wide standardization (irrespective of the standardization that the ALAM accomplished), each of the small firms found itself purchasing very small quantities of specialized parts from a few suppliers. To change vendors for a part like a carburettor or an ignition assembly might mean major design changes.

The suppliers of parts and materials had by this time become dependent on business within the car industry. But this dependence doomed them to remain small firms since there was no scope for the mass production of standardized vehicle parts. Each supplier survived by producing parts in low quantities for a few assemblers. As an example, in 1910, one maker of parts made 800 different sizes of lock washer for the car industry.

The result of this structure was high cost production, attenuated competition, and a mutual dependence between individual suppliers and assemblers that meant that if one failed, its 'partner' probably would as well. Since most of these firms were undercapitalized, this was a real threat, and in the crisis of 1910, this was exactly what happened. Eighteen car manufacturers disappeared along with many of their suppliers.

The cost of a lack of industry-wide standards was more modest to Ford and GM. With higher production volumes and at least partially integrated parts manufacture, they effectively standardized internally. And to the extent that they purchased parts from independent suppliers (e.g. tyres, tubes, carburettors, and speedometers), they did so in volume. This afforded their suppliers some production efficiencies from which Ford and GM could extract price concessions.

Not surprisingly, the small assemblers of cars and their suppliers saw industry-wide standardization of components as the solution to their relative disadvantage. Soon, the small firms—both the car assemblers and the parts makers—came to dominate the SAE's standardization efforts.[14]

Component standardization was clearly in the interests of the small firms, partly to reduce cost and partly to reduce their vulnerability to their partners' bankruptcy. None the less, they still faced many difficult standardization decisions. Which components should be standardized? If variety reduction were the objective, how many varieties were optimal? For example, should all cars have the same tyre size? If there were to be a couple of different sizes, what should they be? At a time of rapid technological change in the industry, when should a design be frozen into a standard? Finally, if standardization of parts was advantageous, and if the small firms were to remain just assemblers of parts, would this not imply that the entire car should be standardized? The solutions to these and thousands of other questions were sought by committees with wide industry representation. When committee agreement on a standard was reached, it was referred to a vote of the SAE membership. Upon passage, the SAE published the standard for voluntary adoption by the industry.

By this process, dimensional standardization started slowly. The SAE began at the same point as the ALAM the previous decade—with spark plugs, carburettor flanges, screw threads, and other fasteners. The number of lock washers in use dropped from 800 to 16, steel alloys from 135 to fewer than 50, and stainless steel tubing sizes from 1600 to 210. Major reductions in variety were achieved in tyres, spark plugs, wheels, flanges, steering-wheel hubs, door hinges, body frames, generator brushes, etc. The first SAE handbook on standards appeared in 1911, and by the mid-1920s it listed about 600 specifications in 100 broad areas including bearings, engine mountings, materials and their testing, headlights, tyres and wheels, fasteners, paints and other finishes, and imitation leathers.

The results of this process of setting standards, although never systematically studied or quantified, are generally thought to be enormous. To cite one specific example:

A well-known manufacturer of parts supplied a score or more of automobile companies. Each one bought from 10,000 to 500,000 parts a year, but each wanted some minor variation in the pattern. The constant change in machine set-up necessitated by these varying demands kept the parts manufacturer's plants in total confusion.

Careful figuring showed him that he could cut his price in half, improve his delivery service and yet make more money himself, if he could induce all his customers to accept the same pattern. One of them saved $4,000,000 a year.[15]

Table 4.2 Automobile firms and production: 1911–22

Year	No. of entrants	No. of exits	No. of firms remaining	Production
1911	3	2	53	199 319
1912	12	8	57	356 000
1913	20	7	70	461 500
1914	8	7	71	543 679
1915	10	6	75	895 930
1916	6	7	74	1 525 578
1917	8	6	76	1 740 792
1918	1	6	71	943 436
1919	10	4	77	1 657 652
1920	12	5	84	1 905 560
1921	5	1	88	1 514 000
1922	4	9	83	2 406 396

Source: Epstein, R. C., *The Automobile Industry*, Shaw, Chicago, 1928, pp. 176, 177, 314.

One estimate put the aggregate industry savings at the equivalent of 15 per cent of the retail value of each car.[16] Another estimated industry savings to be about $750 million annually.[17]

The growing standardization in the period from about 1913 to the end of the decade not only lowered costs of parts and materials, it also accounted in part for the increase in the entry rate into the industry (see Table 4.2). Supporting the process was the fact that car technology had stabilized somewhat, and designs of parts did not have to be constantly changed for technological reasons.

Standards and mass production: Ford's Model T

The American automobile industry in general and Ford's Model T in particular were the first cases of true mass production, and the industry is still the archetype of mass production methods. And whereas mass production is not synonymous with standardization of any particular kind, the two are so closely linked that mass production cannot be analysed independently of an understanding of standardization. Why was the Model T the first example of mass production? And what role did standards and mass production play in the evolving structure of the automobile industry?

Mass production requires the standardization of both purchased and manufactured parts to a degree sufficient to permit perfect parts interchangeability. This parts interchangeability in an assembly line—

or intra-firm standardization—is the single dominant principle of mass production. The ability to standardize parts to this degree is in turn dependent on the development of the technology of tools, measuring and testing instruments, and materials sciences.

The idea of improving production by using standardized interchangeable parts dates back more than 500 years to Gutenberg's movable type and to the Venetians' installation of parts into their galleys in what was perhaps the first instance of 'assembly line' production. The introduction of mechanization in the Industrial Revolution brought mass production closer. Early nineteenth-century examples of primitive mass production include ships' blocks, clocks, and firearms.

All the elements of what we now know as factory mass production were available before this century. In fact, the machinery, the materials, the measuring instruments, and the ideas were not only available but also they had all been tried successfully. Yet the scale on which mass production was carried out in the automobile industry so distinguishes it from everything preceding it that it is generally considered original.

The first public demonstration of vehicle parts interchangeability was given in 1908. Henry M. Leland, General Manager of Cadillac, had three of his cars torn down to their elemental parts, the parts scrambled, 100 parts replaced with stock equivalents, and then the three cars reassembled with only screwdrivers and wrenches. He capped the demonstration by having them driven 500 miles around the Brooklands Speedway.[18] Yet Leland's Cadillacs were not Ford's Model Ts.

In addition to standardized and interchangeable parts, mass production requires a standardized product. Although most producers around 1910 had a 'standard' product or line of products, no one took the principle to the limit that Henry Ford did.

Ford was quoted as telling an associate in 1903 (well before he brought his ideas to fruition):

> The way to make automobiles is to make one automobile like another automobile, to make them all alike, to make them come from the factory just alike—just like one pin is like another pin when it comes from a pin factory.[19]

The Model T was developed in 1907, introduced to the market in 1908, and in 1909 Ford abandoned all models save the 'T'. In his memoires, Ford recalled his thinking in 1909.

Table 4.3   The Model T Ford

Year	Retail price	Sales
1908	$850	5986
1909	$950	12 292
1910	$780	19 293
1911	$690	40 402
1912	$600	78 611
1913	$550	182 809
1914	$490	260 720
1915	$440	355 276
1916	$360	577 036

Source: Rae, J. B., *The American Automobile*, University of Chicago Press, Chicago, 1965, pp. 61.

. . . in the future we were going to build only one model, that the model was going to be 'Model T', and that the chassis would be exactly the same for all cars . . . Any customer can have a car painted any color that he wants so long as it is black.[20]

Ford was the pioneer of mass production, but he owed much to the particular characteristics of time, place, and the automobile market. The elements that made car manufacturing in the United States in 1910 uniquely able to introduce the world to mass production include, first, an extremely large potential market, which existed only in the United States. By comparison, the British car market was so much smaller that it was only in 1934 that the largest British firm, Morris Motors, could justify installing its first moving assembly line. A second ingredient was a market with highly price elastic demand. Thus, the cost savings from more efficient production could be passed on to the consumer to expand the market and justify still further production innovations. Another ingredient was a product of great technical sophistication with many parts, yet one in which the latest precision tooling and techniques could still be applied. Finally, mass production required that there be no organized resistance.[21]

The Model T was, of course, tremendously successful as Table 4.3 shows. It came just as the market for higher priced cars was becoming saturated leaving mostly repeat purchases available in that segment. The Model T opened a huge market of lower income consumers, and for many years the Model T had little or no competition. Ford's assembly lines could send a finished car out the door every three minutes, and by 1920 every other car in the world was a Model T.

Ford's profit was truly phenomenal, and to this day it is perhaps without equal in manufacturing. It was never below an annual 45 per cent of net worth until 1917, and several times it exceeded 100 per cent. Profits declined after 1917 but still usually exceeded 20 per cent of net worth. An investment of $10 000 in 1903 would have been worth about $275 million in 1926!

In addition to production economies for Ford, the standardization of the Model T afforded advantages to consumers. The purchase decision could be made on the basis of an objective criterion like price. The Model T was an extreme example of a complex product sold strictly on a price dimension. Unlike the case of GM cars, which will be discussed below, Ford made no pretence of selling style. Ford announced to buyers that if he sold 300 000 cars in one year, he would rebate between $40 and $60 to each buyer. In 1915 he paid off—$50 to each. Although he would not have expressed it in these terms, he allowed each buyer to share what would otherwise have been an external economy of scale.

Another attraction of the Model T was that it was so standardized and so familiar that it could be repaired without necessarily taking it to an expert. This was especially attractive to consumers in rural areas. And because it was ubiquitous, repair parts were constantly available from wrecked or otherwise abandoned Model Ts.

The particular suitability of cars to mass production can be shown by a brief digression to look at the industry's experience trying to produce aircraft. At the outbreak of the First World War, there was virtually no American aircraft industry. There was, however, an assumption that the automobile industry would be able to apply its physical assets and its know-how to mass produce aeroplanes. It was commonly believed that an aeroplane was just a flying engine in the same sense as a car was just a rolling one. A number of automobile pioneers purchased aircraft firms.[22]

The experience was a dismal failure. What distinguished cars at the time was not the nature of the vehicle (which was perhaps little more than a rolling engine) but the nature of its production. Aircraft turned out to be totally unsuited to the technology of mass production because the total number of units of any one model was so much smaller and because the technology—both of basic aeronautics and of flight combat—was constantly changing. Thus, the potential for standardization was never sufficient to exploit the capabilities of the automobile industry. The automotive industry, *per se*, never did build aircraft in the First World War.

Aircraft engines were different, and here the motor car industry was in its element. The first engines to be considered for American production were European, but they were not designed to sufficiently close tolerances to be mass produced. Each engine required too much individual machining. So designers from the US automotive industry designed a new engine that could be mass produced—the now-famous Liberty engine. Almost all of the 25 000 engines produced during the war were made by the automotive industry.[23]

The 1920s: concentration of the industry
The decade of the 1920s opened with an economic crisis. The crisis of 1920/21 drove many small firms from the industry. In the first half of the decade, 126 firms quit—more than existed when the decade started—while about half that number entered. By the time that the shakeout was completed in the mid-1920s, the large manufacturers of cars had taken over the SAE and the leadership of the standards movement (only Ford still withheld from the movement).

With the demise of many of their small competitors, the large firms (and by 1924, eight makers were producing more than 100 000 cars annually) saw all the benefits of standards and none of the competitive disadvantages. Standards still offered the opportunity to reduce the cost of purchased inputs which were important despite the firms' vertical integration. And standards were becoming increasingly important to the infrastructure that was necessary for the further growth of the industry.

Regarding the standardization activities of the SAE, the agenda of the large firms was different from that of the small firms. The small firms had wanted to standardize many of the components that they purchased but which were produced internally by the large firms. This allowed them to mitigate one of their competitive disadvantages. The suppliers were interested in the same standards. Thus, in the earlier period, standards were set for body frames, flanges, door hinges, steering-wheel hubs, etc. But because the large firms did not purchase these parts, these standards languished in the 1920s in favour of standards for such things as steel and lubricants, electrical apparatus, and tyres—inputs that even the relatively integrated firms bought from outside. In general, standards started to be set by the automobile industry for other industries beyond the makers of car parts.

This shift in the standardization agenda was consistent with the customer's changing needs. As car ownership spread, so did the need for an infrastructure of fuel and service stations. Standardized tyre sizes, petrol grades, lubricants, and electrical components were important here, and the SAE was responsible directly or indirectly for much of this.[24] For example, in 1926, the SAE finalized its standards for oil viscosity.[25]

When the large producers of cars took over the SAE, conflict for the first time occurred between the car makers and their suppliers. A decade earlier, the small car makers and their suppliers were roughly equal in size and united in their vulnerability to the power of the bigger integrated manufacturers who had chosen to ignore the SAE. By the 1920s, automobile manufacturing was America's largest industry, and the suppliers found themselves confronted by very large firms. This was true of the suppliers of manufactured components, but it extended beyond them. The car industry was consuming annually 90 per cent of the nation's petroleum products, 80 per cent of its rubber, 20 per cent of its steel, 75 per cent of its plate glass, and 25 per cent of its machine tools. An industry of this size had the power to dictate standards in many areas, and it did.

This confronted the suppliers with some novel problems. One was the problem of meeting the tolerances written into the specifications of standards by the car makers. The SAE would often reach its required consensus on new standards by setting them to the stipulations of the most demanding of its members. Reluctant though they might have been, the smaller makers of parts and the petroleum, rubber, steel, and other industries had little choice but to acquiesce.

Another problem was with premature obsolescence of capital equipment that occurred when standards were set or changed. As will be discussed in the next section, when consumers started to seek variety in their vehicles, the manufacturers started to differentiate their products. The design changes implied higher production costs and premature capital obsolescence to makers of parts. Conflict over this problem in the SAE is well documented on parts like piston and cylinder sizes, flywheels, and springs.

The relative competitive positions of suppliers were effected as well. Because the standards committees were dominated by large firms within which consensus was necessary, the standards that were accepted did not inflict a disproportionate adjustment burden on any one of these firms. But this desire for fairness did not extend to the suppliers who occasionally experienced windfall fortunes or crises. To give one example, the decision to incorporate roller bearings, and not ball

111

bearings, into the standards had a disastrous impact on those bearing producers that specialized in ball bearings.

Model proliferation and planned obsolescence

. . . in the automobile industry, a delicate balance had always . . . to be struck between a policy of making too few models or 'chassis types' to satisfy the demands of the market and one of simultaneously making too many types to permit a sufficiently economical production and a satisfactory control over manufacturing processes. . . . allowing for . . . individual ineptitudes . . ., the high general level of failures in automobile manufacture remains in large measure due to the great difficulties present in striking a proper balance between sales and manufacturing policies.[26]

By the 1920s, market growth was slowing, and one producer's expansion came more and more from others' contraction. It was becoming difficult to offer a functionally superior car given the commonplace design technology. So competitive strategy turned to more chassis types for each producer and a sacrifice of production economics for the sake of marketing considerations. Between 1923 and 1926, Chevrolet, Overland, Star, and Essex started to differentiate their styles successfully. Ford's sales stagnated in 1923 and 1924, and in 1926 Ford's sales declined in absolute terms.

By this time, sales volumes were high enough that the cost penalty paid by a producer who offered several different models was not insurmountable. Holding prices constant, a manufacturer could raise profits by reducing costs through standardizing on a single model or by raising volumes by offering a broader variety of models. Different makers with different strategies could be identified along this trade-off even before 1920. Ford, Dodge, and Hudson, for example, had narrow product lines, each with few changes over the years. Willys-Overland, Studebaker, and Buick, by contrast, had broader product lines. By the early 1920s, the trend was clearly moving in favour of greater variety at the expense of production economies.

The crisis of 1920/21 prompted another important change in the industry, in addition to the failure of small firms and the growing model variety. This was the appearance of significant competition from used cars. With the recession and the increasing numbers and longevity of automobiles, both the demand for and the supply of cars in the used car market increased. The slow diminution in the number of different producers' cars on the road meant fewer potential orphans, and it meant that spare parts and the know-how to repair cars were both readily available. Used car agencies came into being, and credit was offered for used car purchases.

With growing competition from used cars, the makers of new automobiles introduced the policy of yearly new model introductions. General Motors was the first to do so (motivated in part to counter the success of the Model T), but it was soon followed by other producers. Although this policy is now known as *planned obsolescence*, originally the annual variation was as much technological as stylistic.

Planned obsolescence, or planned non-standardization of a model through time, had a number of consequences. One was to renew the primary market annually by providing newly styled cars to style-conscious buyers. But this was not all that happened. Buyers of new cars, in turn, sold their older cars sooner than they would otherwise have done. This increased the supply of used cars on the market and reduced their prices, increasing the number of cars in operation at any given time. In an efficient cycle, the developing used car market and the ancillary operations necessary to support older cars in operation (like the service business) made it easier for buyers of new cars to sell their older cars each year. One can again see the disadvantage of the small producer. Consumers would fear—and it could become a self-fulfilling prophecy—that failure of the used car market would leave them with an unsaleable orphan.

Another, possibly unintended, function of the annual model change was to insulate the car producers from the competition of independent makers of parts in the spare parts market. All the car makers profited disproportionately from selling spare parts (and still do today), and it was in their interest to keep independent producers of parts from entering that market.[27] With fewer units of more models on the road, it was harder for independent firms profitably to duplicate the tooling of the original producers. This was not the case, however, for a car like the Model T. So many were produced that independent makers of parts entered the repair parts market and undermined Ford's profitability. Probably 50 per cent of all car repair parts were produced by independent firms in the 1920s, and most were for the Model T.[28]

Ford shunned both the multiple-model line and the annual model change strategies. By the mid-1920s, the Model T was suffering from its technological obsolescence as well as from its success. It had been produced for 18 years with little change except for the addition of a self-starter and some improved materials. Having been produced with little change for so long, it was too common to appeal to relatively affluent consumers. Although it could be purchased in a variety of colours in the 1920s, it was still the standardized car. The only efforts to differentiate it were those of third parties who made upgrade kits to improve engine performance. When, in 1927, the last Model T was made (serial number 15 007 003), Ford had no replacement available.[29] Chevrolet became the number one car in sales and rarely relinquished that title until recent years.

The two policies illustrated by Ford and GM show again how doomed were those small producers who still existed in the industry in the 1920s. They were unable to achieve the economies of mass production that Ford had achieved, and they could not offer the variety of models and styling changes of GM. Although there were some entrants into automobile manufacturing in the 1920s, none survived. The number of producers of automobiles in the United States dropped from 108 to 44 between 1923 and 1927. With the formation of Chrysler in 1925, the 'Big Three' structure of the industry began to emerge.

By the late 1920s, GM controlled Buick, Cadillac, Olds, Chevrolet, Oakland, Fisher Body Company, Yellow Truck and Coach Manufacturing Company, and 16 parts and accessories companies. It also owned General Motors Acceptance Corporation and a number of export and overseas companies. Ford, the most integrated vertically, was into steel making, foundries, saw mills, freighters, and railways. Ford and GM were head and shoulders above the other makers, yet the industry was never the monopoly that either the steel or oil industries were at the time. The desire for a variety of models perhaps had a major role in preventing such a monopoly. The Model T was the closest the industry ever came to being dominated by one firm and even by one model of car. In 1921, Ford peaked at 60 per cent of all cars in the United States and Canada, and it ultimately declined in part because of its ubiquity.

B ANALYSIS

The beginnings of the industry

In 1890 there were three ways to power automobiles—steam, gasoline, and electricity—and of these, one was patently inferior to the other two: gasoline.[30]

One of the most intriguing questions that might be asked about the automobile industry is whether the petrol engine on which the industry standardized was the best technological choice. It was shown in the case study how the tremendous range of technological options slowly diminished in the first decade of the industry, and much the same process occurred in the other cases in this book. With what confidence can one conclude that this common weeding out phenomenon results in a good standard?

Unfortunately, the answer is 'very little'. Referring to the principles presented in Chapter 1, standardization embodies economies of scale. The more a standard is adopted, the more attractive it is to users and possibly to producers as well, and the more likely it is to achieve further adoption until it dominates its market. There is many a caveat to this story, of course, but the story is still a powerful one.

The implication is, however, that all a technology may need to become dominant is a headstart. It is natural to assume that the dominance of the petrol engine came from its inherent superiority, and thus that its past and even present universality is well deserved and socially beneficial. Such need not be the case, however, if its headstart came for reasons of chance (or even of merit). From an initial headstart, the focus of producers and users on the petrol engine—on its use, on its progressive improvement, and on the infrastructure to support the driver of a petrol-powered car—could make it the best technology available. But this is not to say that had steam or electricity obtained the headstart, they would later have been replaced by petrol. They might have developed to become superior to today's petrol engines.

Might steam, in fact, have proven superior to petrol in the long run? That is a question that this study cannot answer. But the steam cycle is thermodynamically superior to that of petrol engines, and experimental steam engines today can outperform petrol engines on the criteria of mileage and exhaust emissions. It is not impossible to imagine that had steam technology benefited from the thousands of millions of dollars of development that has been spent on petrol engine technology, its superiority might now be overwhelming.

What chance might have accounted for the headstart of the petrol engine? In 1895, a petrol-powered car won a well-publicized race (with only six entrants) and indirectly may have inspired the 'Curved-Dash' Olds, which the case noted was the first car 'model' produced in quantity. Was the steam engine perhaps killed by an historical occurrence? Steam was a viable contender with petrol until an outbreak of

115

foot and mouth disease led to the removal of horse watering troughs—the most prevalent water source for steam cars at the time. The steam car lost popularity then and never recovered.

None of this proves that bad luck bequeathed us the story recounted in this chapter or the blessing (or curse) of the motor car as we know it now. But it does illustrate how the interrelationship between standardization and technology can lock inferior technologies in place. If the specifics of the automobile industry leave the reader unconvinced, the case of the QWERTY keyboard—designed to minimize typing speed to avoid jamming mechanical typewriters—might be more convincing.[31] The dominant design of US nuclear power plants, FORTRAN, the British railway track gauge, a.c. electricity, and the US colour TV standard are other examples of allegedly inferior technologies becoming locked in by early chance events.[32]

The importance of standardization to the nascent industry

The particular characteristic of most of the standards in this industry—a characteristic that accounts for the cooperation in setting standards and which makes this story an important one—is that they were non-proprietary. The standardized dimensions of screw threads, wheel rims, flanges, and many other parts entailed no ownership rights. Thus, many of the strategies observed in the other cases in this book, cases in which standards were based on proprietary technologies, were not possible here. Each firm in the automobile industry was free to adopt or reject proposed standards, no firm could exclude others from use of 'its' standards, and standards developed only if virtually all firms saw adoption as beneficial.

That the automobile industry should be a paragon of cooperative development of inter-firm standards should not be surprising. Two characteristics were important. The first is the number of different parts and materials subject to scale economies that were used in common by many firms in a rapidly expanding market. In the early days of the industry, most automobile 'producers' were simply assemblers who contracted with others to produce components. Their motive for standardization was to reduce variety and to lower purchase costs. Secondly, the durability of the automobile required a repair parts network. Thus, standardization of parts not only afforded production economies but also distribution and inventory economies.

There is another aspect to non-proprietary standards in automobiles. The placement of the controls in an automobile is so customary that a driver can step into virtually any car and drive it away. The most obvious aspect of this standardization is (for most of us) the left-hand positioning of the steering wheel, but standardization also extends, for example, to the placement of the foot pedals, the instrument controls, and the dashboard displays. At first glance this may not appear to be a case of multi-product compatibility standards, and various writers on standards would not regard it as such. Yet all the principles applicable to questions of compatibility standards apply here equally well once one sees this as a case of compatibility between physical and human capital. Analogous cases of compatibility (or incompatibility)—between products and trained operators appear (frequently with the introduction of new models) in industries such as aircraft (with cockpit design and flight performance), computers (with software), typewriters or computer keyboards (layout), engineering or scientific instruments, etc.

It is interesting to contemplate how the motor industry's structure would have evolved had each firm designed the controls and other operating features of its cars to maximize the difficulty that an owner would experience were he or she to switch to another make. As we will see in the next chapter, the computer makers did just this. They could do so because their designs were proprietary and they could legally prevent copying by others. In the motor industry, copying could never be prevented, and so one observed *de facto* standardization of what in computer terminology would be called the 'user interface'.

The Seldon patent and the ALAM

As the previous section noted, this industry is important because most of its standards were non-proprietary. There are two reasons why. One is that the technology was principally mechanical so that many of the standards (screw threads, wheel rims, etc.) were dimensional and therefore not patentable. The other reason is that after their experience with the Seldon patent litigation, the firms chose to cross-license their otherwise patentable technologies. Thus, they consciously and collectively chose to renounce competitive use of proprietary standards.

Why did this industry abandon the use of a competitive weapon that we have seen eagerly grasped in many other industries? Certainly, part of the reason was the frustration of its recent court battles and the desire to avoid their repetition. But there may be additional reasons. No single firm at the time saw any clear competitive advantage accruing from a patented technology. The way firms distinguished themselves in the subsequent years was via production efficiencies and model styling,

117

neither of which was patentable. In fact, the technologies on which the automobile rested were not amenable to much patent protection once the court gave a narrow interpretation of the scope of the Seldon patent. It is significant that although the patent sharing agreement allowed an exclusion for 'important technologies', no such exclusion was ever granted.

The episode of the Seldon patent was beneficial to the industry's development in another way—it provided the revenues for the industry's creation of standards. Free riders like Ford and the other non-licensed producers could not doom the standardization effort given the ALAM's charter and the way it chose to execute it.

How valuable was the ALAM's standardization effort *per se*? As the case described, there were two sides to it. Once was to reduce the variety of purchased components. The evidence is that this was very important not only to the industry in general but also to all the firms in it. At the time, little distinguished ALAM members from non-members (except that the latter were free riders on the former's investment in standardization). Most bought the same types of components from the same independent supplier industries, so there was rough competitive symmetry.

Might the early standardization of fasteners, spark plugs, and other parts that were the focus of the ALAM and the SAE have had a deleterious impact on variety or on a design engineer's creativity? Probably not. The biggest problem at the time, and the concern of the early setters of standards, was *purposeless* variety. Quoting Howard Coffin, then the President of the SAE:

> Every purchasing department in the business is being seriously hampered in its work by the lack of uniformity in the material specifications, which are being passed on to them by our engineering departments. . . . Individuality of design is one thing and should be encouraged. Individuality in specifications is largely useless and should be restricted within reasonable limits. . . . It is the little things—the little things which are different merely because they are different and for no good reason—which keep the purchasing departments in hot water and delay production. Nine times out of ten it is not the unavoidable act of Providence which delays the output—it is the irresponsible draftsman or designer who is permitted to draw upon his imagination for specifications throughout the entire range of theoretical possibilities.[33]

Despite this impassioned criticism, however, Coffin and others were sensitive to the risk—which appeared more seriously later—that standardization would inhibit technological advancement and limit valuable design freedom. It was Coffin himself who, when a suggestion was made to standardize flywheels, said, 'If you standardize the flywheel, I believe there will be no limit beyond which you might not go'. Another President of the SAE complained that, 'If we are going to say what the bore or stroke of a motor is to be then there is not much chance for making any of the revolutionary changes made abroad recently'.[34]

By contrast, the ALAM's quality standards were less valuable to the industry even though they were probably not deleterious. Quality standards do not feature significantly in this book, focused as it is on compatibility standards. None the less, it is interesting to observe in passing how quality standards can be abused. Indeed, there are numerous examples of antitrust cases that show such abuse.[35] Whether or not one believes that the ALAM was intent on excluding entrants to achieve monopoly, the potential to use quality standards towards that end is evident. It is clear that the ALAM's policy was ludicrous. To demonstrate that his product would satisfy the required quality standard, Ford would necessarily have had to violate the ALAM's interpretation of the Seldon patent. Yet the evidence is that quality standards had little structural impact on the industry.

Standards in small and large firms

If it is true, as argued above, that variety-reducing standardization had no competitive implications before 1910, what changed in the following decade? The answer, of course, is that there was no longer competitive symmetry. And we see here that even non-proprietary and industry-wide standards can have competitive implications if the firms start in asymmetric situations. Differences in firm size, in the extent of vertical integration, in the installed base of capital, and in design philosophy can all cause conflict over standards, both among car makers and between them and their suppliers.

The competitive disadvantage of a small non-integrated firm is clear. There was an input cost disadvantage (at a time when purchased inputs were a major portion of total cost), and there was as well a risk consequent on the reliance of each small firm on other small firms. Because of the weak capitalization of all these firms—and thus their high failure rates—this was a serious problem. There may have been another aspect to the problem as well. In situations in which a single supplier is dependent on a single customer and vice versa—situations of simultaneous 'lock-in' and 'hostage'—the possibility always exists that one firm would try to exploit the other. History does not identify this as a problem in the early days of the motor car, but standardization that would give each firm—supplier and buyer—multiple market opportunities would attenuate such a problem if it were to exist. It would put the small non-integrated firms on the same footing as the integrated firms that did not face the problem. (In fact, recent research has shown that car firms systematically integrate to produce in-house those components where this problem of mutual dependency would otherwise be greatest.)[36]

Inter-firm standardization around a limited number of varieties of purchased components was a very practical step for the small firms to alleviate their disadvantage so long as the cost of agreeing on the standards did not outweigh the benefits. We will see other cases in which alliances of small firms seek to benefit by inter-firm standards. There would surely be some conflict among the firms that would require negotiation. Changing flange dimensions for carburettors, for example, would mean design changes for those firms whose engines would no longer fit the flange. But designs were in any case evolving rapidly, and much of the cost would have been borne by the makers of parts rather than the assemblers. Since the smaller manufacturers of parts were also major beneficiaries, they still supported the standardization. In general, the high value of standards, the common interest of the small firms working within the SAE, and the lack of any significant investment required to create the standards (e.g. when compared to what is required in many electronics industries) all made the setting of standards by the small firms feasible.

What was the attitude of the large manufacturers of cars to the standardization movement pioneered by the smaller firms? Evidence that comes from membership of the standards committees and from other sources shows that they neither boycotted nor supported the movement. In general, they were indifferent. Why?

There are a number of explanations for the indifference of the large manufacturers. Although they were relatively integrated, their integration was incomplete. Since they still bought vast quantities of parts and materials from independent suppliers, industry-wide standardization would reduce their costs just as it would reduce the costs of the small firms. So there was at least one motive for the large firms to support standardization. On the other hand, they presumably knew that the SAE's standardization work would proceed without them (as it did), so that when they wanted to take advantage of standardization, they could do so for free. Since the standards were non-proprietary, there was no way by which the smaller firms that supported the SAE could exclude the large firms from taking a free ride. (This is a point that reappears in the next chapter on alliances of small firms on open standards in the computer industry.)

At the same time, however, there are a number of possible reasons why the large integrated firms might have opposed standardization. For one thing, it levelled the playing field on which both large and small firms competed. The large firms might well have imagined themselves better off with slightly higher prices for purchased inputs and less competition than with lower input costs and a more competitive industry. This would be especially true to the extent that their market power as buyers afforded them acceptable purchase prices regardless of inter-firm standards.

The second reason why the large car firms might have shunned industry-wide standardization is that it would reduce their design flexibility and product differentiation. Although this might not have been a major constraint in 1910, it became more serious as product differentiation appeared. An integrated car producer, free of industry-wide standards, is free to alter its design as market or technological changes require. The small assemblers, reliant on standardized purchased parts for cost efficiency, had a motive to reduce differentiation and to freeze their standards unless or until an industry consensus for a change could be reached. There was actually a proposal on the part of the small firms that the entire automobile be standardized. The proposal was for ten models of automobile, each with a standard wheel base, suspension system, radiator, fuel feed, etc. The positioning of the models in what we would now call 'product space' was not designated. The proposal was never accepted.

The largest suppliers of parts, in contrast to the large makers of cars, were generally hostile to standardization. Their reasoning was explained by one of the early principals of the SAE, P. M. Heldt.

. . . a reduction in number of sizes [of parts and materials] is evidently of much less importance to the maker who is already well established and prepared to furnish practically all sizes normally called for, than to the newcomer. Hence it was feared by some of the large concerns that standardization would over-stimulate competition by making it too easy to get into the business.[37]

Given that large and small firms purchased many parts and materials in common, why was any explicit and formal standardization necessary? Why did not the small assemblers simply 'standardize' by deciding individually to use the same parts designs and materials specifications as their larger competitors did? (They might still have suffered a price differential due to smaller purchase order sizes, but that problem would exist regardless of what they did.) In other words, the small firms could have been free riders on the large firms' parts and materials specifications, creating in the process industry *de facto* standards. It is an ironic reversal from what is normally expected that in this case, the large firms adopted standards that the small firms set through the SAE.

Could the large firms somehow prevent the small firms from adopting their parts designs? If the large firms owned the vendor's tooling, it is possible, and it has occasionally been seen in the analogous instance of spare parts. But in general, it would have been difficult for the large firms to block small firms' access to the independent suppliers. The surest way to stop such *de facto* standardization would have been for the large firms to increase their upstream vertical integration and thus bar the small firms from access to standardized parts. This would have forced the small firms to organize a collective effort to standardize.

What attitude should the large firms have to the standardization of important repair parts? If the parts were produced by the firms, one would expect them to resist standardization because it would allow independents to enter the lucrative spare parts market. However, if the parts were produced by distinctively different industries (examples include tyres, light bulbs, etc.), standardization would be beneficial to large firms as well as to small firms, not so much because of its impact on their input costs but because of the development of the repair infrastructure.

In summary, a company like Ford would have very different views regarding standards depending upon the parts concerned. It would not want standards for doors, door hinges, and bumpers, for example, because it made those parts internally. It would probably be indifferent to industry-wide standards for washers and many fasteners that it purchased for its car assembly in large enough volumes to get good prices irrespective of industry-wide standardization. Finally, it would favour standards for tyres that it purchased for its assembly operations and which were also important spare parts.

Standardization and the repair parts market

Standardization of car parts allowed the entry of independent producers of spare parts in a way that is analogous to IBM's experience with its System 360 standardization (to be recounted in the next chapter) and for the same reasons. In both cases, the producers had a strategy of price discrimination that earned them substantially higher margins in the tied product (car spares or computer peripherals).[38] In both cases, the strategy worked only as long as entry to the network was denied to other producers. But in both cases, standardization allowed that entry (often called 'cream-skimming' entry) and thus undermined the strategy.

In the car industry, one way by which independent producers of parts could be kept at bay was to reduce the total volume or the rate of production of any particular repair part to fewer than the minimum efficient scale of production for an independent producer. As long as repair parts were non-standardized across different firms, from one model to another within a single producer's model line, and from one model year to the next for any single model, the demand for spares could be kept below that which an independent producer of parts needed to justify investing in the tooling. The car firms have generally been sensitive to this, and even in the mid-1960s, 25 per cent of all components (in value terms) faced no alternative source of supply save the original producer.[39] Ford suffered the most from standardization that allowed independents to enter the spare parts market, and there is evidence that Ford's profits dropped from the 1910s into the 1920s and 1930s because of it.

Conclusions

The automobile industry is a case of high collective interest in standardization yet low firm-level interest in any *particular* standard. Standardization of fasteners, for example, was of great value to the industry, but the particular specification of a fastener that was decided upon was of relatively little interest to any single firm. So cooperation in setting standards was easy, at least compared to other cases in this book.

The standards were also relatively cheaply produced since they were dimensional rather than an inherent characteristic of a costly process of technological development. It is for this reason that they were not given patent protection. There were two immediate consequences. First, the problem of free riders was never significant. There were free riders—Ford, for one. But it made little difference to the standardization process. Second, there was rarely a strong vested interest on the part of a particular firm that 'its' standard should be chosen by the industry, and no firm had the power to exclude others from unilaterally adopting 'its' standard. As was shown, this did not mean that public domain standards were (or generally are) competitively neutral. Multi-firm standards were an advantage for the small non-integrated firms compared to larger competitors—a theme that appears again in the next chapter. But public domain standards surely mitigated many problems of collective standards-setting such as will be seen next.

In the VCR case, there was also a strong common interest in a single standard. Yet in that case, the industry witnessed intense conflict between companies, which was only relieved with the market victory of one and the defeat of the other. Why the difference with the automobile case? In VCRs, the standards were the property of individual firms and the source of their profits. The vested interest each had in its own technology prevented them from fashioning an institutional arrangement that would obviate what was a long and costly inter-standards war.

In the early period of mainframe computers (Chapter 5), there was low collective interest in industry-wide standardization and high firm-level interest in a particular standard. The result was a structure of incompatible standards coexisting in harmony until the market environment changed in the 1980s.

Notes and references

1. The Society of Automotive Engineers, which will be discussed in more detail in this chapter, has been so successful that its standards are no longer confined to the automotive industry but apply to aeronautical and marine industries as well. The SAE was instrumental in establishing the organization that later became the American Standards Association.
2. Quoted in Epstein, R. C., *The Automobile Industry*, Shaw, Chicago, 1928, p.91. A further handicap was the poor road system. In 1900, there were only 200 miles of paved road outside of the cities in the United States.
3. Seldon had applied for the patent in 1879. Had the normal course of events transpired, it would have been awarded in 1881 and would have expired in 1898 before motor car design had coalesced around the petrol engine. But at the time, an inventor was allowed to file repeated amendments that delayed patent issuance without jeopardizing a claim to priority. The reader might imagine how the story of the industry would have differed had the Seldon patent expired before the turn of the century.
4. The name of the company is ironic since its venture into electric vehicles was unrelated to the Seldon patent and was a disaster.

5. This royalty dropped to 0.8 per cent in 1907.
6. The ALAM also standardized the formula for calculating horsepower rating, later commonly used for taxation.
7. J. B. Rae, for example, takes a critical view in *The American Automobile: A brief history*, University of Chicago Press, Chicago, 1965. Epstein, *op.cit.*, defends the ALAM.
8. Interestingly, the only car that was ever produced to Seldon's original patent design was built specifically to be introduced as evidence in the court case.
9. Had the court ruled against Ford, it would have made little difference since the patent was due to expire in 1912. Ford might have been required to pay retroactive royalties, but by this time he could easily have afforded to do so.
10. This organization became the Automobile Manufacturers' Association in the 1930s.
11. Fortunately, the potential exclusion of 'major' innovations never caused any industry conflict. Only one petition for exclusion was received in the first 10 years of the agreement, and it was denied. By the mid-1920s, not a single patent suit had been filed among the NACC members.
12. This became the Society of Automotive Engineers in 1917.
13. Ford had agreed to sell his company to General Motors for $8 million in cash in 1909. GM's board approved the purchase, but the company's financial backers on Wall Street vetoed it, arguing that the price was too high.
14. See Thompson, G. V., Intercompany technical standardization in the early American automobile industry, *The Journal of Economic History*, Winter 1954, pp.1–20. Note that the discussion in this section concerns standards set by producers for their own use. However, there was at least one instance in which consumers tried to set standards. The Car Club of America, organized by a group of New York bankers with the intention of reducing the price of high-quality cars, tried to set purchase standards for a car to be produced by Merchant and Evans, a Philadelphia firm. But the venture collapsed.
15. National Industrial Conference Board, *Industrial Standardization*, National Industrial Conference Board, Inc., New York, 1929, p.171.
16. S.A.E., *Fortune*, August 1948, p.140.
17. National Industrial Conference Board, *op.cit.*, p.166.
18. Exactly 50 years before Leland's demonstration of interchangeable auto parts, essentially the same demonstration was performed with 10 muskets.
19. Quoted in Rae, *op.cit.*, p.59.
20. Ford, H., *My Life and Work*, Doubleday, New York, 1923, p.72.
21. Because mass production threatened the livelihood of skilled artisans, it was often fought. In France at the time of the Revolution, such resistance ended efforts to mass produce muskets with interchangeable parts.
22. For example, John N. Willys bought control of Curtiss, and a syndicate of

automobile interests headed by Edward A. Deeds of Delco created the Dayton-Wright company.

23. To support the argument here, it is worth noting that although the engines were mass produced by the automobile industry, the total quantity looks very small compared to the number of Model Ts shown in Table 4.3.

24. The SAE dedicated an entire meeting in 1923 to the task of putting the service business on a sound commercial basis.

25. The SAE's lubricant grading system is still used, and numbers like SAE 10W30 are familiar to most drivers.

26. Epstein, *op.cit.*, pp.171, 173.

27. Producers at the time could require that their dealers carry only parts they supplied and not those supplied by independents. Ford and Dodge had a policy of inspecting dealers' spare parts inventories without advance notice. Practices of this sort are forbidden now after a long line of cases tried by the Federal Trade Commission.

28. National Industrial Conference Board, *op.cit.*, p.192. This issue of pricing of spare parts is examined in Crandall, R., Vertical integration and the market for repair parts in the United States automobile industry, *Journal of Industrial Economics*, July 1968, pp.212–34.

29. It was not until the 1930s when Ford introduced the Mercury that the company had cars in all price ranges.

30. Arthur, W. B., Competing technologies and economic prediction, *Options*, April 1984, p.10. The analysis here is drawn from this paper. See also Arthur, Positive feedbacks in the economy, *Scientific American*, February 1990, and Competing technologies, increasing returns, and lock-in by historical events, *Economic Journal*, March 1989.

31. David, P., Clio and the economics of QWERTY, *American Economic Review*, May 1985.

32. See Arthur, *Economic Journal*, *op.cit.*

33. Coffin, H. E., S.A.E. succeeds mechanical branch of A.L.A.M., *Automobile*, **XXII**, 1910, p.979.

34. Both quotations appear in Thompson, *op.cit.*, p.17.

35. Examples include the Radiant Burners, Standard Sanitary, ASME Water Valve, and Trenton Potteries cases. See Shenefield, J., Standards for standards-makers, unpublished address to the American National Standards Institute, 1978.

36. Monteverdi, K. and D. Teece, Supplier switching costs and vertical integration in the automobile industry, *The Bell Journal of Economics*, Spring 1982.

37. Heldt, P. M., The S.A.E. at twenty-five, *Automobile Industries*, **LXII**, 1930, p.802.

38. Crandall, *op.cit.*, has shown that the margin and return on capital invested are both dramatically higher in the car parts business than in car sales.

39. Crandall, *op.cit.*, p.225.

5. The European open systems movement in the computer industry

A   CASE STUDY

Introduction

The case of mainframe computers represents a sharp contrast to the case of microcomputers covered in Chapter 2. Mainframes have long been the domain of proprietary and incompatible hardware and software systems and have never experienced an episode of *de facto* standardization like that which occurred in microcomputers.

Yet there is now a growing movement, especially in Europe, towards industry adoption of 'open', that is, non-proprietary system standards across all segments of the industry (with the exception of microcomputers). This movement, if successful, will fundamentally break the industry tradition and cause the most significant restructuring in the industry's history. The attempts of various consortia of firms to establish open standards in lieu of proprietary standards are the subject of this chapter.

This case will allow us to examine a number of important competitive issues in standardization. The first is why *de facto* standardization has not occurred here to the extent that it has in microcomputers. A second issue, and the main focus of the chapter, is whether small firms can form an alliance around multi-vendor standards and then use those standards to 'level the playing field' on which they compete against dominant firms' proprietary alternatives. This strategy is in sharp contrast with the more common strategy for small firms (which caused *de facto* standardization in microcomputers) of emulating dominant firms' standards. We will see that these small firm alliances pose complex and often unexpected problems, and their outcome is even now uncertain. Ironically, large firms have to some extent usurped the movement, and competition between these large firms to lead the open systems movement appears to have subjugated its original goals.

Underlying this issue is a more fundamental one. What are the relative advantages and disadvantages in high technology industries of two very

127

different processes of standardization? One is formal multi-firm agreement. The other is *de facto* standardization by a dominant firm. Because there are few other instances in which these two processes are in such direct competition, the case of open standards in computers is an extremely important one for us to understand.[1]

Other important issues appear in this case as well. One is the need to devise incentives or organizational structures that can cope with the inevitable problem of free riders that was discussed in Chapter 1. Another is the need to assure approximate competitive symmetry in an open systems alliance so that all parties have a sincere motive to support it. This is a particularly difficult challenge here because open system standards, should they succeed, will have a major impact on the computer industry's structure and form of competition, and this implies that firms must forecast their future competitive environment and prepare strategies to succeed in it.

The success or failure of the open systems movement will have important public and private sector policy implications for this and other industries where standards are important competitive variables. It will, of course, determine the extent to which a computer user will be freed from dependence on one supplier's proprietary standard. And it will affect significantly the industry's growth and competitiveness. More generally, this case can teach us something about the prospects for open systems in other high technology industries where proprietary standards have traditionally existed and still are observed.

Standardization in the history of the computer industry

Because proprietary systems are still marketed—even by proponents of open systems—it is important to understand how competition between them has proceeded over the life of the industry. Should the initiative to replace them by open systems fail, the industry is likely to revert to the traditional form of competition that will be described in this section.

Electronic computers were first developed in the mid-1940s, and for the first 20 years or so of the industry's life, there were no significant efforts to introduce standards. Computers were all incompatible, not only from one manufacturer to another but even within individual manufacturers' product lines. For example, in 1960, there were 50 different tape drives with tape widths that ranged from half-inch to two inches, and the tapes had from 7 to 48 data tracks. There were 60 different internal codes for assigning binary digits to alphabetic characters, 11 of which were used by IBM. And IBM alone had six incompatible full computer systems on the market.

Although this was the structure into which the industry grew through the 1950s, the structure slowly began to change in the 1960s. The first industry standards appeared in high-level programming languages. The earliest programs had to be written in binary code for the specific hardware on which they ran, and thus they could not be standardized. But in 1956, IBM developed FORTRAN, a machine-independent programming language that allowed programmers to write programs in mathematical and logical notation. These programs were then electronically translated into binary form for different kinds of computer hardware. FORTRAN became widely accepted for writing scientific programs, but it was not well suited to commercial applications.

A commercial analogy to FORTRAN was first proposed in 1959 by the US Department of Defense. An industry-wide group of manufacturers and users working under the sponsorship of the Defense Department published the specifications for COBOL in 1960. Although large firms like RCA and Univac embraced COBOL, IBM—taking what would become a familiar posture—refused to accept it, preferring to develop a proprietary alternative. Nevertheless, IBM announced that it would participate in the COBOL group. IBM's ambivalence ended when the US Government Services Administration (GSA) indicated that COBOL would feature as a criterion in letting government contracts in the industry. IBM then abandoned its own language and adopted the industry standard COBOL.[2]

The story of communication standards is roughly similar to that of COBOL. In 1959, the American Standards Association formed a subcommittee to set standards for the binary coding of alphabetic and other characters. IBM was a member, but when the final proposal for a code called ASCII was ready, IBM voted against it and against virtually the entire industry. Again, IBM had an alternative (called EBCDIC). The company was eventually forced to offer ASCII when the federal government, frustrated by the delays in reaching a voluntary accord, established ASCII as a federal purchasing standard in 1968. Even then, IBM continued to obstruct efforts to promote ASCII, and it continued to offer EBCDIC in addition and in preference to ASCII. (Many of IBM's major products had translators to convert back and forth from EBCDIC to ASCII.) In fact, IBM's undying support for EBCDIC cursed the company into the 1980s when connectability between computers became an industry *sine qua non*, and IBM found itself left behind the ASCII standard's bandwagon.

In the core of the mainframe computer business, the first cracks in the structure of competing proprietary standards appeared in 1964 when Honeywell introduced its 'IBM-compatible' H-200 model line. The H-200 was a direct competitor of IBM's 1401, the world's most popular computer at the time. The H-200 was significantly better than the 1401, however, with a more powerful central processing unit (CPU) and superior peripherals. Although it was not internally compatible with the 1401, it was offered with a software package called the 'Liberator', which transcribed 1401 programs and files to the H-200 system.

The H-200 strategy was radical, and it would have been more successful than it proved to be had its timing been better. Only four months after the H-200 appeared, IBM introduced the 1401's successor, the system 360, that forever changed the nature of competition regarding standards in the industry.[3]

The System 360 was a family of computers (its different models varied in power by a factor of 1000) that brought internal product line standardization to IBM. System 360 computers shared design philosophy, language, and peripheral connections, and they brought the 70 per cent of the mainframe computer market that IBM controlled under a single standard.

In retrospect, the System 360 strategy was a brilliant one, but at the time there was some dissension about it within IBM because of the risk it implied. The 360 was less compatible with the 1401 than was the H-200, and the 360 and H-200 were completely incompatible. So there was the risk that 1401 customers would upgrade to the H-200 and forever shun the path that the 360 would take. IBM made an effort to mitigate the risk by developing an emulator that allowed the 360 to run 1401 software, although it did so very inefficiently. Still, the emulator allowed 1401 customers to convert to the System 360 progressively rather than all at once.

The System 360 turned out to be tremendously successful. It offered IBM enormous economies of scale and scope by spreading both software and hardware investments over a range of products. A larger software market justified higher investment in more and better software that in turn sold more hardware in an efficient cycle. At the same time, standardization afforded major servicing efficiencies in this service-intensive industry. Finally, IBM could now announce upgrades piecemeal rather than having to go through the wrenching experience of periodic major new system releases. Users benefited not only from more applications but also from reduced operator and programmer training costs and from new-found flexibility to modify or upgrade their systems. System 360 reduced the uncertainty that users faced about where IBM's product development would take them. At the same time, however, IBM's customers were exposed for the first time to a large switching cost differential between upgrading within the System 360 family and upgrading to another vendor's hardware. The phenomenon of lock-in first appeared.

Unfortunately for IBM, this successful standardization and the consequent growing network of System 360 customers provided the motive and opportunity for other firms to enter the market by designing products in conformance with the 360's standardized specifications. These products were of three sorts: one was a complete IBM-compatible system; the second was a 'plug-compatible' peripheral product like a memory unit or a disk drive; the third was a compatible CPU.

RCA was the first to attempt to build a system—called the Spectra 70—that was compatible with the 360's repertoire of software. But the attempt at compatibility was botched, and the 360's software had to be rewritten to run on the Spectra. Later, when IBM introduced the System 360's successor, the System 370, RCA faced the dilemma of following the 370 and thus abandoning the Spectra's customers or upgrading the Spectra and thus abandoning any possibility of IBM compatibility. Faced with such an unattractive choice, RCA sold its computer business to Sperry Rand in 1971.

A second class of compatible products was the computer peripheral. IBM's strategy with the 360 was to draw new customers into the IBM world with low prices and margins for 'entry level' variants of the 360. The customers, once locked in by the high switching costs, were then taken through an upgrade path with expanded memory and peripheral products for which IBM charged high prices and earned high margins. Peripheral equipment (including expanded memory) typically constituted more than half the cost of a large installation. This strategy of price discrimination made it attractive for plug-compatible manufacturers (often referred to as PCMs) like Telex and Memorex to enter the markets for the peripherals that could be easily connected to the standardized IBM mainframes. Entry was made especially easy because plug compatibility allowed prospective customers to try the PCMs' equipment at a modest installation cost and with a simple exit route should the equipment not work as hoped.

The PCMs made significant inroads into IBM's installed base, starting in 1969, but IBM did not take their entry seriously until the GSA indicated in 1970 that it intended to convert government installations from IBM's to PCMs' equipment.

IBM's competitive response to the entry of the PCMs consisted of a number of pricing, design, and marketing changes intended to frustrate plug compatibility without sacrificing the standardization that had made it possible. As a generalization, prices were cut in peripherals and raised in CPUs because of the differential entry barriers in those different markets. System elements were bundled or unbundled depending on what was most appropriate to the competitive challenge, interfaces were changed, and IBM introduced a multi-year peripheral lease policy with a large price discount. These changes in 1971 and 1972 effectively marked the end of the PCMs as profitable competitors. In 1973, they had about 5 per cent of the installed base of hardware in the United States. The changes also provoked a number of antitrust suits that IBM either settled out of court or won.[4]

The PCMs went after the market for peripherals that attached to IBM's CPUs. Another strategy, rendered particularly attractive by the price changes that IBM introduced to combat the PCMs, was to sell a superior CPU that could be linked to the PCMs' peripherals and that could run IBM's software. The first to do so was Gene Amdahl, formerly IBM's Director of Advanced Computer Systems and thus someone intimately familiar with the Systems 360 and 370. Starting work in 1970, he introduced an IBM-compatible machine in 1975 that was more powerful than the System 370 but equal in price. With a significance that is still felt today, Amdahl was forced to give Fujitsu a 24 per cent stake in the company in order to finance his venture (even though the strategy of entering only at the stage of the CPU reduced the financial burden of entry).[5] Fujitsu also manufactured the hardware. Other firms like Itel followed Amdahl's lead with Hitachi manufacturing the Itel hardware.

Not only has IBM's hardware been copied, but so has its operating system software. The principal firms to do so were Fujitsu and Hitachi.[6] At MITI's insistence, the two firms agreed in 1971 jointly to develop a line of IBM compatibles. Fujitsu took advantage of its partial ownership of Amdahl to get the technology that Hitachi then got from Fujitsu, from public sources, and from industrial espionage. This allowed them to develop and sell an operating system that was functionally equivalent to that of the 360/370.

Thus did standardization start to appear in computers—partly through the work of industry groups, partly by IBM's internal standardization, and then partly from the efforts of individual firms to emulate IBM's standards.

Another force that increased *de facto* standards was the progressive shakeout of firms in the industry. By the mid-1960s, half the major producers of the previous decade had left the field, and IBM had become the industry's largest firm.[7] But the consolidations in the decades of the 1950s, 1960s, and 1970s did not immediately reduce the incompatibility problem. The reason was that the departures were via sales to surviving firms who were then left with increased internal non-standardization. Honeywell, for example, had become the second largest firm in the industry by acquiring the computer operations of Raytheon (in 1957), General Electric (in 1970), and Xerox (in 1975). But despite its market share, the company did not have the internal standardization that IBM had, and thus it gained few of the associated economies.[8] The same result occurred with the Burroughs/Sperry merger, which created Unisys, and with ICL in Europe, which was created with the mergers of English Electric Computers, ICT (both of which had themselves grown by merger), and Plessey's computer operations. Only over an extended time did the reduction in the number of companies reduce the number of incompatible systems on the market.

IBM's dominance of mainframe computers led the US Department of Justice and the Commission of the European Communities to file major antitrust cases against the company. The US Justice Department brought its monopolization case in 1969, charging IBM with predatory pricing and predatory investment. The case was abandoned as unwinable in January 1982.[9] The European Commission case, filed in late 1980, alleged that IBM abused its dominant position in the European market[10] by bundling main memory with its computers' central processors and by protecting the design details of new product interface specifications until shipments started. The case was settled in August 1984 with IBM's agreement to release System 370 interconnection information earlier so that makers of compatible equipment would not suffer a competitive disadvantage.

Although IBM has consistently claimed—and outsiders have generally agreed—that its accord with the European Commission did not hamper it, none the less, IBM has lost strength in Europe recently both to European rivals like Siemens and to US firms like Digital Equipment Company (DEC) and Hewlett-Packard. IBM's share of the market dropped from 25 per cent of all computer-related sales in 1985 to 22 per cent in 1986 and 19 per cent in 1987. Market shares were stable in 1988.

Once relieved of the burden of defending itself against the US antitrust prosecution, IBM sued both Hitachi and Fujitsu for violating its mainframe operating system copyrights. The case against Hitachi was settled out of court in 1983. The Fujitsu case was settled by compulsory arbitration in 1988. The arbitrator ruled that Fujitsu had to pay IBM $833 million, but that in return—and in order to encourage competition in the market—Fujitsu could have very restricted access to IBM's future software releases. Thus, Fujitsu was freed to sell an IBM-compatible operating system in competition with IBM.

The story that has been told above is one of increasing but still incomplete *de facto* standardization around IBM's mainframe hardware and software systems. But along with this slow process of standardization, another process occurred that took the industry in the opposite direction. New firms entered the industry above and below IBM's model range (the range within which some *de facto* standardization was occurring), and this entry introduced still more incompatible standards. DEC entered in 1957, and by focusing in the early 1960s on academic and scientific demand for minicomputers, it introduced its own new and incompatible system standards (the VAX-class of machines). Control Data Corporation (CDC) entered the industry with scientific supercomputers. From their entry points, both DEC and CDC have pushed their incompatible standards into the range of IBM's offerings.

IBM responded to DEC's threat in minicomputers by introducing a succession of models starting in the early 1970s. The company's thinking, which was a complete reversal from that which motivated the System 360, was that each model should be optimized for the niche it was intended to serve even though that implied incompatibility both with IBM's other computers and within its minicomputer line. In retrospect, this strategy of standards variety rather than compatibility and connectivity proved a disaster, and it allowed DEC, whose machines were all compatible, to grow even through the industry slump of 1985/86. IBM has had to dedicate much of the 1980s to reversing the mistake.

Even though producers were in general selling incompatible systems, users were not necessarily doomed to being supplied by one system monopolist or another. In fact, most large firms had multi-vendor procurement policies (policies that became progressively more widespread through time) and they could and did mix and match system elements by jury-rigging gateways, either by themselves or with the help

134

of specialist firms.[11] Multi-vendor compatibility was thus often achieved, but not by standardization.

In conclusion, and despite the degree of *de facto* standardization that has been discussed, the structure of the computer industry in the mid-1980s could fairly be characterized as one of competing incompatible proprietary systems. IBM held slightly less than 50 per cent of the world-wide market for information processing (almost the same as it had in 1956), DEC was second with about 10 per cent, Unisys was third with 7 per cent, and each of the others had 6 per cent or less. Fujitsu and Hitachi, which could crudely be described as IBM compatible, shared about 11 per cent of the market between them. It was into this competitive environment that the open systems movement came.

The decade of the 1980s and growing competitive pressure on small firms

The decade of the 1980s saw intensified competition in the world-wide mainframe computer industry. Profit rates slipped below the industrial average, growth rates slowed, and mergers began to consolidate the industry. All of these are characteristics of industrial maturity, and computers, now about 40 years old, are in some respects becoming a mature product. But despite the evidence of maturity, the technology is still changing rapidly, and the rate of cost reduction in computing has not diminished. This would normally guarantee a continuing regeneration of the market even if strictly from replacement demand. Unfortunately, there are some problems peculiar to computers that have curtailed demand growth and increased the competitive pressure especially on the small producers.

First, the growing power of ever smaller machines has depressed hardware prices and stimulated the most rapid growth in the market segments of those small machines—microcomputers, minicomputers, and technical workstations. In general, these segments are the most competitive (mainly because they are the most standardized), and thus they have lower profit margins than mainframes. Microcomputer gross margins average about 40 per cent, for example, compared to 60 per cent for mainframes. As product lines shifted to smaller machines, the return on equity of 15 major firms tracked by Salomon Brothers, Inc., dropped below the Standard and Poors 400 stock index. This market shift to smaller machines was particularly worrisome to firms like Unisys, NCR, Honeywell, and most of the European firms because they were at least relatively strong in mainframes.

135

Second, as computing power became cheaper, the constraint on increased productivity shifted to software. In short, computing hardware capacity exceeded the requirements that existing software could generate, and this retarded hardware purchases until software development could catch up.

A final contributor to the slowdown was growing customer frustration with incompatibility between components of their systems—systems whose boundaries were continually expanding functionally and geographically. This frustration was commonly reported in the business press. One example was a cover story in *Business Week* entitled, 'The Computer Slump: The Industry's Problems Run Deeper than Boom-and-Bust Cycles.'[12] The article attributed the slowdown in part to two factors that relate directly to standards. One was stated as 'Most customers want all their computers to communicate in order to raise productivity—but the technology isn't there.' Second, 'Lots of companies have been burned by buying different brands of computers that can't understand one another.' That is, users were frustrated by incompatibility within a single firm's product line as well as by incompatibility between different firms' products.

Lower profitability, slower sales growth, and excess capacity of perhaps 20 per cent focused the attention of smaller firms on how to survive an anticipated industry shakeout. Continuing the traditional policy of developing and selling proprietary products began to look increasingly untenable. Hardware and software development costs were too high, and customers were more and more reluctant to commit to the proprietary products of small producers. All of this and a more aggressive IBM, free of the antitrust cases that had inhibited it for years, threatened to accelerate the convergence to IBM's standards in the marketplace. Facing this prospect, the smaller firms—in particular, the European firms—turned to open system standards alliances as a survival strategy.

The open systems movement
'Open systems' is an imprecise term. One difficulty is that it is used either to imply non-proprietary standards or to imply proprietary standards that are 'open' to any firm paying a non-discriminatory licence fee. The communications standard, OSI (Open Systems Interconnection), is an example of the first use of the term. OSI is a standard developed by international public bodies (the International Organization for Standardization (ISO) and the International Telephone and

Telegraph Consultative Committee (CCITT)), and it is in the public domain.[13] MS/DOS is an example of the second. As was explained in Chapter 2, it is the proprietary development of Microsoft, but it is available to any firm paying a non-discriminatory royalty.

The term 'open systems' generally implies three kinds of standardization. One is standardization of the interface between computers and their applications software. This standardization, which is partly hardware standardization and partly standardization of operating systems, should allow applications to be 'ported' (i.e. moved) from one computer to another. This porting should be possible between different manufacturers' computers and possibly between different model sizes (e.g. between minicomputers and mainframes) as well. It should be possible to port applications from an older vintage of computer to a newer vintage.

The second kind of standardization is of the communications interface. This should allow different computers to communicate directly with each other, for example, by moving data and messages within an electronic mail system.

The final standardization is that of interfaces between computers and peripherals. This should allow the mixing and matching of various kinds of hardware in a network by facilitating physical connection.

The principal open systems groups

There are numerous inter-firm groupings in the open systems movement. They differ in a variety of ways including their function (whether they simply choose and validate existing standards or whether they actually invest in the creation of new technologies and standards), the composition of their members (in particular, whether they are dominantly American, European, or Japanese, and whether they include users or not), their form or organization, and the particular standards they have chosen to support.

The groups that we will consider here—X/Open, UNIX International, and OSF—are major ones in the industry, but they are not the only ones.[14]

The X/Open Group

The open systems movement started in Europe in 1984 when X/Open was founded as an independent non-profit consortium of European computer vendors including Bull, ICL, Nixdorf, Olivetti, Philips, and Siemens. The objective of the founders was stated as follows:

137

The X/Open Group's principal aim is to increase the volume of applications available on its members' systems, and to maximize the return on investments in software development made by users and independent software vendors. This is achieved by ensuring portability of applications programs at the source code level. Through this portability users can mix and match computer systems and applications software from many suppliers, and thus investment in applications software is protected in the future.[15]

In other words, the stated objective was voluntary agreement on an open multi-vendor standard in the computer industry. The unstated motivation for this alliance of relatively small computer firms was to use open systems as a competitive weapon to 'level the playing field' with the more powerful American firms'—especially IBM's—proprietary systems.

Ironically, however, X/Open's founders were soon joined by some of those more powerful American (and Japanese) firms whose applications for admission could hardly be denied by an organization dedicated to industry-wide cooperation. First DEC joined, and later membership expanded still further to include IBM, AT & T, Fujitsu, Hewlett-Packard, NCR, Nokia, Sun, and Unisys. X/Open is now the broadest open systems organization in terms of the scope of the standards it supports (software, communications, and languages) and its geographical reach (it has offices in the United States and Japan as well as in Europe).

The basis for X/Open's multi-firm standardization was OSI, a number of computer languages including C, FORTRAN, and COBOL, and the UNIX System V operating system. OSI was in the public domain, and the computer languages were all widely accepted as open standards. But UNIX System V was proprietary to AT & T, and this has created problems.

UNIX is a computer operating system originally developed for in-house use by AT & T's Bell Laboratories in the late 1960s.[16] Although a proprietary creation, AT & T licensed UNIX widely and freely as a result of a 1956 consent decree with the US Department of Justice.[17] Licensees commonly adapted UNIX to suit their own needs and then often re-licensed their own proprietary versions of it. There were perhaps 20 different UNIXs in use in the mid-1980s including Xenix (Microsoft), Ultrix (DEC), and Sinix (Siemens). Although each was based on a UNIX core that originated with AT & T, many were nevertheless

138

incompatible. X/Open hoped that out of this chaotic situation would come agreement on a common base for applications software (similar to what MS/DOS could offer to microcomputer software applications). Until the schism that will be discussed below, the common assumption was that AT & T's UNIX System V would be the unifying UNIX standard.

UNIX was well known and accepted in the engineering and technical segments of the industry, but it was rarely seen in general business use before the open systems movement awoke interest in it.[18] UNIX's characteristic virtues (although they were not unique to it) were its versatility (it had been implemented on computers ranging from top-end microcomputers to large mainframes[19]) and its capability for simultaneous use by many people (i.e. its multi-user and multi-tasking capability). In 1984, the UNIX market was worth $2000 million with approximately 100 000 UNIX-based systems in use. In 1988, about 600 000 copies of UNIX were in use, and 10 per cent of all computers sold the previous year ran on it. Forecasts for UNIX's market growth were high. For example, the International Technology Group predicted that sales of UNIX-based systems to *Fortune* 500 firms by 1992 would number 935 000. International Data Corporation forecast a UNIX market share world-wide of 20 per cent in 1993.

X/Open's 1988 budget of approximately $19 million was composed of $17 million in subscriptions from its members and $2 million generated from sales of its publications and from other activities. X/Open had a permanent staff of about 20 professionals, perhaps 150 people from independent firms working under contract (in marketing or software consulting, for example), and another 200 people in members' own organizations working in X/Open-related technical groups.

Once standards agreements were reached, X/Open's permanent staff would incorporate those agreements into what was in 1989 a seven-volume *X/Open Portability Guide*. This was the official guidebook for how to make the compatible hardware and software to which member companies were pledged. These standards were referenced by public bodies like the Commission of the European Communities in purchasing guidelines for member countries. A number of individual European governments such as Sweden and the United Kingdom have officially adopted the standards as well.

X/Open recently started a programme to test and certify compliance with its standards. The objective was to release a directory identifying and promoting compliant products irrespective of whether they were produced by member or non-member firms. X/Open has received pledges from software companies including Microsoft, AT & T's Data Systems Group, Lotus Development Corporation, and Cullinet Software, Inc., to support X/Open in their developments.

Recapturing the standard: AT & T and UNIX International

Resolution of the US Justice Department's antitrust case against AT & T in 1984 left the company free for the first time to enter the computer industry. Over the next four years, its Data Systems Group lost over $2000 million (including $1000 million in 1986 and $400 million in 1987) and completely failed to give AT & T a significant place in the industry.

But UNIX was a potential bright spot. It accounted for 6 per cent of the world's $87 000 million computer market in 1987. Its stronghold was the popular mid-range scientific computing segment, but it was seeing new applications across all size ranges. It was especially strong in Europe with an approximate 12 per cent market share, bolstered in part by European governments' preference for the open standards of European organizations like X/Open rather than the proprietary standards of US multinationals.

AT & T's strategy for UNIX's future had concerned the proponents of open systems ever since UNIX was first considered as a possible open system standard. Their concern rose with time as AT & T became more aggressive in its dealings with licensees. For example, Geoff Morris, X/Open's chief executive, complained that, 'AT & T needs to clarify publicly its position on standards and to end the confusion over its verification system.'[20] Another concern was AT & T's edict that software producers must conform exactly to its specification for interfaces between UNIX and applications programs. This requirement could readily be extended to other functions like communications, data management, and user interfaces. But in addition to specific concerns such as these, there was general apprehension about the future that AT & T envisioned for what was simultaneously its proprietary system and the choice of the open systems movement.

In January 1988, some of that uncertainty was dispelled, but not reassuringly. AT & T announced that it would buy 20 per cent of Sun Microsystems (later raised to 29 per cent) and would officially designate Sun to develop UNIX.[21] AT & T's announced objective was to raise its share of the computer market from 2 per cent in 1988 to 7–10 per cent by 1991. This was to be driven in part by UNIX development and in

140

part by advanced minicomputer models based on a chip that Sun would provide by the end of 1989. The deal with Sun and other concurrent deals that AT & T struck brought three leading versions of UNIX (AT & T's System V, Sun's, and that of the University of California at Berkeley) under AT & T control.

The link between AT & T and Sun prompted a host of firms whose applications and user bases were dedicated to AT & T's version of UNIX to form an organization called 'UNIX International'. The 29 founding members including Sun, Amdahl, Control Data, Fujitsu, ICL, NCR, Olivetti, Prime, Unisys, and Xerox. Its objective was to speed sales of UNIX-based computers and in particular to support AT & T's UNIX development.

The revolt of OSF

The single event that precipitated a revolt from AT & T's attempted leadership of UNIX was its acquisition of part of Sun. But conflict within the UNIX ranks had been building before this. A major schism developed when the US Air Force demanded that bidders for one of the largest computer contracts ever let by the government offer AT & T's UNIX System V standardization. DEC, IBM, and Wang protested, arguing that their version be specified (or at least accepted as an alternative). Their protest failed and AT & T won the contract, valued at nearly $1000 million and as much as $4500 million if the full authorized procurement budget were spent.

So AT & T's agreement with Sun and its growing power over the UNIX market succeeded in provoking a revolt. The alienated firms met in 1988 at DEC's West Coast research and development facility, and OSF (the Open Software Foundation) was officially created. OSF was a non-profit corporation founded by seven US and European firms: DEC, IBM, Apollo, Groupe Bull, Hewlett-Packard, Nixdorf, and Siemens. Membership was open to anyone, however, and by the end of 1988, there were 67 members, both American and European. Some firms, for example Intel, Motorola, Data General, and Toshiba, joined both OSF and UNIX International. OSF's start-up funding was $121.5 million.

OSF ostensibly wanted to create a truly open and competitively neutral UNIX. This was the objective of the open systems movement from the beginning, but in the view of the OSF members, the objective had just been frustrated by AT & T. Once formed, OSF immediately set out to create a 'new' UNIX—one that it would own and license in a non-discriminatory way. The new UNIX would be based on IBM's

141

version of UNIX, called AIX, rights to which OSF purchased from IBM. AIX was incompatible with AT & T's System V.

With substantial funding and a charter to write software (as opposed simply to validating standards as was the case with X/Open), OSF will in principle live off the revenue generated by its software licences. Evidence at the time of this writing is that OSF intends to use a strategy of low price to promote its standards in competition with UNIX International (and to a lesser extent Microsoft's OS/2).[22]

B   ANALYSIS

The principal questions to be answered in this analysis of open standards in the computer industry are the following:

1. Why did so little *de facto* standardization take place in this industry in the decades leading up to the open systems movement?
2. What precipitated the European movement? Why did it start in the mid-1980s rather than earlier?
3. Why are there different and 'incompatible' open systems organizations?
4. How do the various organizations attempt to deal with the inevitable problems of free riders and competitive asymmetries that accompany open systems? In what ways might their attempts be improved?
5. What is the future of the open systems movement? Will it prove to be futile or will it fundamentally alter the nature of competition in the industry?
6. In general, what are the advantages and disadvantages of collectively set standards versus standards set by a single firm in industries in which technology is costly to develop?
7. If open systems become a reality, how will the competitive environment in the industry change? Who will benefit and who will lose? How will firms re-establish competitive positions once the strategy of locking customers into proprietary technologies is no longer possible?

Background to the open systems movement

The computer industry has long been notorious for the multiple and incompatible standards that have made the industry a high-technology

Tower of Babel. A comparison is often drawn between computers and telecommunications to highlight the relative lack of computer standards. It is a telling comparison but it is more than that: it also provides an explanation for the contrast.

Telecommunications standards were set either by state-owned monopolies (in most of the world) or by a government-regulated but privately owned monopoly (in the United States), and they were set in a stable technological environment. This accounts for the almost universal absence of incompatibilities (even though the interfaces between different countries' systems were often patched together by gateways rather than truly standardized). The computer industry, by contrast, always consisted of many producers competing in an unregulated and technologically more dynamic market. The rapidly changing technology, the relatively large number of firms, and the lack of a powerful industry association naturally inhibited industry-wide agreement on standards. Furthermore, the industry's relatively competitive structure meant that competitive advantage could be gained by technological and thus standards differentiation, and that cooperative research and development was threatened—at least in the United States—by antitrust prosecution.[23]

Thus, it is natural that the industry developed an early competitive *modus operandi* of incompatible systems and little formal or spontaneous standardization. It is reasonable to believe that this resulted not so much from a conscious strategy to lock customers into proprietary technology, but more from the unconstrained technological experimentation in the firms such as that which took place in the videotape recorder industry. Yet with such strong network economies of standardization, this initial proliferation of incompatible systems, which carried on through the late 1950s, created a naturally unstable situation. One could expect it to be followed by a process of standards convergence of one kind or another as the industry and the technology matured. But how would the convergence take place? Would there be a widespread cloning of a dominant standard as occurred in microcomputers? Would standardization come from the commercial failure of the rivals to the largest network standard as in VCRs? Or might standardization result from formal industry-wide agreements as in automobiles?

In the early life of many industries, one firm emerges with a substantially larger market share than its competitors. What brings this initial lead may be superior technology, good business judgement, or just good luck. Regardless of what it was in computers, our starting

143

point in analysing the process of standardization will be the situation in the late 1960s when IBM was the dominant producer and the other firms had assumed much inferior positions.

An obvious question to ask is why there was so little evident consolidation of networks in the decade of the 1970s? Why was it not until the mid-1980s that structural change began?

The answer is that each competitor was satisfied with the *status quo*, and any unilateral move would only threaten the mover. There were obvious design obstacles to cloning another's standard. Computer mainframe technology was sufficiently complex that compatibility could fail for purely technical reasons as the case of RCA's Spectra showed. Efforts to appropriate another's technology faced legal barriers as the Hitachi and Fujitsu cases demonstrated. The overall market was growing rapidly so that even the small firms were prospering, and their installed bases were expanding to make a standards conversion ever more difficult. And finally, it was not until the 1980s that the demand for connectivity dramatically increased the value of network economies and thus the competitive advantage of very large networks.

So each firm in the 1970s was tempted to play the same game as did IBM of locking its customers into its product line and earning monopoly rents. The result was a rough stalemate between systems producers in which the various incompatible standards coexisted. In VCRs, by comparison, the competition between Betamax and VHS never reached a stalemate because the bandwagon favouring VHS started to roll before Betamax could build a large installed base of pre-recorded films.

This early stalemate in the computer industry was described by Brock as follows:

> So long as no firm is making specific compatibility attempts, each can act in a semi-monopolistic manner. The possibility of a largely noncompetitive industry with reasonably stable market shares among the main participants seems to be becoming a reality. To the author's knowledge, no specifically competitive campaign with compatible equipment has been mounted since RCA left the business in September 1971.[24]

Brock's description of the US industry was accurate when written in 1975, and it could have applied equally well to the European situation a decade later.

144

Table 5.1 European computer producers (1986)

Company	Computer sales world wide ($m)	Per cent of sales in Europe	Per cent of sales in national market
Ericsson	1344	89	n.a.
Groupe Bull	2568	94	66
ICL	1756	81	63
Nixdorf	2075	92	52
Olivetti	3865	70	37
Philips	1763	87	n.a.
Siemens	4387	88	65

Source: Flamm, K., *Creating the Computer: Government, industry, and high technology*, The Brookings Institution, Washington DC, 1988.

Pressure on the small European firms and their strategic options

The open standards movement was at first uniquely European. As a stylization, the mainframe computer industry there in the early 1980s could be characterized as one in which IBM competed with the individually much smaller European firms, each of which had some hegemony in its own domestic market. Collectively the Europeans constituted a market share of about 65 per cent in 1986 sales (yet only about 25 per cent of the installed base). The size of the European firms is indicated in Table 5.1.

This industry structure had been in a quasi-equilibrium in the sense that market shares had been roughly stable for some years as Brock described. IBM had the advantage of a large network of customers sharing the concomitant network economies. Each of the smaller European firms had a network of locked-in customers that was sufficient to provide adequate monopoly rents in a growing market. These networks had been built and sustained over time by a combination of geographic segmentation, accomplished when the network economies in the industry were relatively low, and from government favouritism, exercised directly via public procurement and indirectly through government influence on private sector purchase decisions.

But the quasi-equilibrium began to break down in the 1980s as was described in the case study. For the Europeans, all the problems described there were exacerbated by a diminishing willingness and ability of governments to champion national firms. Further, the prospect of more open public procurement in connection with the Community's '1992' programme augured declining market shares and fortunes for the Europeans. Well aware of their predicament, the European firms could contemplate a number of defensive strategies:[25]

1. *They could surrender and join the dominant (IBM) network.* The literature on standardization suggests that whereas large firms will generally prefer proprietary standards, small firms will prefer to seek network economies by adopting the standard of the dominant firm (to the extent that they can).[26] Standardization in microcomputers is a good example of this, and an important question is why the same result was not observed with mainframe computers.

For one thing, microcomputer standards developed from the designs of the industry's suppliers who offered their components and complementary products to any and all who were willing to pay for them. So the operating system and the various chips, memory modules, and disk drives were in effect 'open standards' from the beginning and were easily adopted once the PC bandwagon started. By contrast, firms in the mainframe industry were vertically integrated, manufacturing electronic components and other hardware items, writing software, assembling systems, and providing full service support. So even relatively small producers like ICL and Honeywell had proprietary control over and substantial commitment to most parts of their systems.

Secondly, as the case explained, Fujitsu and Hitachi had from an early date tried to join the IBM network by a variety of methods ranging from the former's investment in Amdahl to the latter's industrial espionage. But their limited success illustrates some difficulties with the strategy. Only if a firm's design or production technology can consistently match or exceed that of its target is the strategy possible. Otherwise, it is vulnerable to competitive price cutting with no defensive product differentiation. Fujitsu and Hitachi were strong in both semiconductor technology and in manufacturing. The Europeans, by contrast, were unable consistently to stay ahead of IBM's technology, and it is unlikely that they were more efficient manufacturers.

Another potential problem is timing. If its design cycle is wrong, the compatible producer may constantly find itself introducing a compatible shortly before the target is introducing the next major upgrade. This occurred vividly with Honeywell's H-200 and may occur again with IBM's recent competitive moves in the arena of operating system competition with Fujitsu and Hitachi.

Finally, the legal obstacles that IBM threw in the path of the Japanese were only one of several reasons to suspect that the Europeans might not have obtained unimpeded access to IBM's network had they wanted it. IBM had increased its rate of new product releases. This would handicap IBM-compatible manufacturers unless they were guaranteed immediate access to important technical information. But the resolution in 1984 of the European Commission's antitrust case against IBM, which ostensibly required timely disclosure of interface information, disappointed competitors and afforded little reason to believe that the competitive situation would be changed via public policy.

2. *European firms could develop conversion (gateway) technologies.* This would link the small firms' standards networks to the dominant standard. But for technological reasons, opportunities to do this were available to a limited degree only, and each of the European firms would require a different gateway.[27] A further drawback to this strategy was that it would free each small firm's established customer base to predation by others.

3. *Firms could increase the size and market attractiveness of their individual networks.* The small firms could, for example, increase their own and/or third-party investment in applications software and other complementary products. Similarly, they could improve the functionality of their products within their existing proprietary standards. But while feasible in principle, no major technological breakthrough was evident, and each firm's individual resource base for research and development would be inadequate to compete with larger and financially stronger rivals.

4. *Firms could enter the market above or below IBM's product range.* They could do this sufficiently confident that non-compatibility would not be a hindrance. This was the strategy taken by DEC and CDC. DEC succeeded in the minicomputer market, which was at the time a relative standards vacuum where scientific and academic applications did not rely on extensive files and existing programs and where many users were themselves programmers. So lock-in was never as significant with scientific and academic users as it was with business users.

Interestingly, IBM's response to DEC was not only weak in terms of products, but in addition IBM made a critical mistake of introducing internal product line incompatibility when communication

147

between computers was about to become vastly more important than previously.

5. *They could merge their computer operations.* Mergers were occurring in the United States, but through the last decade there was little evident interest in mergers in Europe. What had occurred, for example, between Honeywell and Bull and between Olivetti and AT & T was, of course, not between European firms.[28] And since a merger would not consolidate standards' networks, it would not (at least immediately) relieve the small firms of their major handicap—networks that were too small.

6. *Firms could create an alliance among themselves around an 'open' alternative standard.* This strategy, intended in the words of its architects to 'level the playing field', was perhaps by default embraced in the mid-1980s by most of the European firms, and it initiated the open systems movement in the international computer industry.

The prospects for open systems standards

Multi-firm standardization, that is, open systems standards, seemed to offer the small computer makers a way out of their predicament just as it did the smaller automobile producers in the early 1900s as explained in Chapter 4. Multi-firm standardization could give access to a potential future network roughly the size of IBM's. It had all the same advantages on the supply side, plus in computers it had an additional advantage on the demand side of appealing to customers wanting to avoid capture. It was, in short, just what the industry needed. Before the 1980s, however, the sorts of organizations that open systems required simply had not been created in Europe, and they were proscribed by the antitrust laws in the United States until those laws were relaxed in the Reagan years.

The open systems movement has now achieved enough for it to be regarded as a serious threat to the historical dominance of proprietary standards in the industry. All producers in the industry are now members of one open systems group or another, and users (in particular, government bodies both in Europe and in the United States) are becoming more and more insistent on open systems in their procurement specifications. As a result, all producers can and do offer products conforming with open system specifications, even though most simultaneously offer proprietary competitive products. So there is an identifiable, albeit small, bandwagon moving in the direction of open systems.

Yet open system standards are a long way from winning the battle.

In fact, the battle has yet to be fought. On one side of the battlefield are the dominant firms with large proprietary networks—and with significant infiltration of their enemies' ranks. On the other side are coalitions of the smaller firms (but including the large firms as well). Each coalition member has an installed base of users tied into its proprietary system (which is still being sold), yet collectively the members are offering a 'new' open standard with only a small existing network. To complicate the picture further, the open standard (UNIX) is not entirely open. It is proprietary, and it may turn out to be offered on unequal terms to coalition members.

The developing competitive battle will take place simultaneously at three levels. At one level, it is competition between firms: dominant firms versi ~es of (mostly) smaller firms and competition between the small ~et position within the alliances. At a second level, it ~ypes of standards: proprietary versus open. A ~een alternative ways of setting standa protection versus committe lytical purposes, we ystem standards alli ompetition.

to create an open efficiency the non-al) technology that uming that non-pro-displace existing pro-lard in their place. The itive advantage *vis-à-vis*, while at the same time ithin the alliance. These challeng

CREATING A PUBLIC D
In virtually all cases of standa high-technology industries, the standards are inextricably tied to he technologies and thus are extremely costly to develop. If the standard and thus the intellectual property embodied in the technology is truly to be in the public domain, then one confronts the familiar free rider problem. Why should a firm invest its own resources to develop technology and standards that are made available not only to all members of the open standards alliance but to non-members as well?

There are a number of ways to answer this question—that is, to mitigate the problem of free riders—and they will be discussed below. Interestingly, however, the open standards groups have tried to avoid the problem altogether. They have embraced standards that were already open, at least to some degree, either by virtue of historical chance (in the peculiar case of UNIX) or because they were developed by public bodies (in the case of the communications standard, OSI).

X/Open's choice of an operating system standard was effectively constrained to exclude IBM's systems for reasons previously noted, to include only existing operating systems for reasons of timing, cost, and marketing, and to exclude the proprietary operating system of any major European producer because of the competitive implications between the members. This left it with few choices. MS/DOS was competitively neutral, but it did not have the functionality that was required for more powerful machines.[29] OS/2 had the functionality, but it appeared only after X/Open was started. Furthermore, the choice of Microsoft's OS/2 would have favoured IBM since OS/2 was developed cooperatively by the two firms.[30]

So the choice was UNIX. It existed, it had an established reputation and user base, it was competitively neutral between X/Open members,[31] and it was at least relatively open. AT & T had rights to it, but AT & T did not seem in the mid-1980s to be as obdurate a competitive adversary as IBM. Yet UNIX had some drawbacks, too.

One of the principal limitations of UNIX was that although it had existed for many years, it lacked some important operating features sought by users. Examples included security measures like record and file locking, checks and audit trails, and a real time processing option. To increase UNIX's appeal, these and other features would have to be provided. And this is where a dilemma arose. The X/Open Group did not have the charter to invest members' contributions to develop these features. Yet without an X/Open investment, there was a risk that individual members of X/Open would see these missing features as avenues by which to differentiate their market offerings and create their own proprietary version of UNIX. The result would be marginally increased functionality but still a number of incompatible proprietary UNIXs—precisely what X/Open hoped to avoid.

A second drawback was that although UNIX has an established user base, that base was concentrated in scientific and technical applications on mid-range computers. UNIX had yet to become established in commercial data processing.

Another drawback to UNIX was that no one knew just how much of it was proprietary. 'UNIX' was a trademark of AT & T, but the term was widely used to describe a class of generic operating systems. Portions of UNIX could probably have been claimed to be in the public domain, and the fact that UNIX was licensed when AT & T was under the consent decree might have been a legal avenue to keep it open. But it would have required litigation to clarify the issue.

Finally, no one knew what strategy AT & T would pursue with UNIX. The company could progressively restrict UNIX purchase agreements and raise prices to control the standard's development and extract rents. Doing so, however, would risk user groups abandoning AT & T's UNIX System V for a more open variant (as eventually happened). Alternatively, AT & T could freely or inexpensively disseminate information and hope to benefit from market expansion, especially towards a widely accepted alternative to IBM. Of course, should it do this, AT & T might later try in some way to exploit other producers' dependence on its standard.

How could the firms mitigate the free rider problem? If different firms had conflicting preferences regarding choices of standards (within the framework of UNIX), they would each have a motive to join and contribute to X/Open to express those preferences rather than risk taking a free ride on a standard they did not like.[32] However, the conflicting preferences that are necessary to overcome free rider problems in this way might prove too great to resolve by negotiation within the organization. Since there was no explicit system of side payments in X/Open (or in any of the open systems organizations), this was a potential problem. In the end, of course, conflicting preferences resulted not in willing participation in a common alliance but in the splintering of the open systems movement into two camps.

Another way to solve the free rider problem would have been for X/Open to acquire full rights to UNIX from AT & T (as OSF did for AIX). It could then have granted non-discriminatory UNIX licences to the members whose subscriptions financed the rights acquisition. Presuming that UNIX had greater value as a single unified standard than as a fragmented one, it would have been to AT & T's advantage to sell the rights. Differential royalties between members and non-members could cope with potentially free-riding non-members. X/Open would have to be run at arm's length from any single manufacturer, but if it owned rights to UNIX, royalty income could give it the financial independence necessary to control the development of the standard.

Basically, the model is that of Microsoft in microcomputers—a quasi-monopolist in control of a standard that is provided on equal terms to all. In this case, however, the firm in control of the standard would be owned by its downstream users.

If the new open standards groups faced free rider problems with standards that were already in existence, they would surely face greater problems with the next generation of technology when heavy investment would be required. An obvious solution would be via cooperation on research and development—cooperation facilitated by European Commission industrial policy[33] and a tolerant competition policy. But this could only be a partial solution because each firm would still face the temptation to assign its least productive personnel to a task the benefit of which would be shared.

Alternatively, members could promise, tolerate, or fail to prevent some market advantage accruing to the dominant investor in the technology, non-proprietary though it may be. A further possibility, and one that is often observed in cases of *de facto* open standards, is to build industry standardization out of assemblies of 'off-the-shelf' technologies or even components. The PC standard was an example. Of course, with the exception of cases like UNIX and OSI, these technologies and components are invariably proprietary to upstream firms. And the structural result of their adoption as the core of the industry's 'open' standard would be to transfer monopoly rents to upstream firms and simultaneously to expose the members of the open standards alliance to intense intra-standard competition.

Perhaps the most attractive strategy for the firms would be to create new corporate entities upstream and at arm's length from themselves with significant financing and a charter to invest in the development of the standards. These upstream firms would then lease their patent rights to members and possibly to non-members. Monopoly rents would accrue to the founders in proportion to their ownership stakes. This was, of course, the concept behind OSF. Yet OSF was flawed from its very beginnings because it was not neutral regarding its prospective customers. It clearly favoured firms like DEC and IBM to the detriment of AT & T, Sun, and the firms that cast their lot with UNIX International.

ESTABLISHING A *DE FACTO* OPEN STANDARD IN THE MARKETPLACE

Assuming that a standard has been selected, how does one promote it into a market? One can explore this question using a variant of the

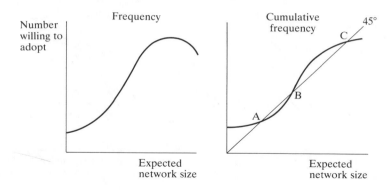

Figure 5.1 Frequency distributions

'tipping model'.[34] Assume that there is a frequency distribution of potential customers whose willingness to adopt the open standard will depend *inter alia* upon how many others are expected to adopt it. In other words, demand for the standard depends on the expected future size of the standard's network. This expectation, in turn, depends in part on actual adoption decisions observed in the market. This frequency distribution is shown on the left of Fig. 5.1. Note that, as shown, a few customers will adopt the standard even if no others are expected to do so.

From this frequency diagram, one can construct a cumulative frequency distribution as shown on the right of Fig. 5.1. The equilibrium will be determined by the intersection of this curve and the 45° line (which is the locus of points where expectations are consistent with reality).

Since the adoption of the standard is by assumption irreversible, one starts at the left and moves to the right along the cumulative distribution curve as adoptions by some prompt adoptions by others. One meets a first stable equilibrium at point A. At this point, adoption will stop since no additional consumers want to adopt the standard given the network size (i.e. given the number of customers who have already adopted it). Here the standard will have achieved only a low penetration rate. But if the expected adoption rate can somehow be boosted sufficiently to pass point B, the network's growth should spontaneously restart and continue up to the second and much higher equilibrium point C.

Ways in which the open standards group can improve its market share
How can the open standards group improve its prospects for achieving high penetration? Basically there are two ways. The first is to shift the

153

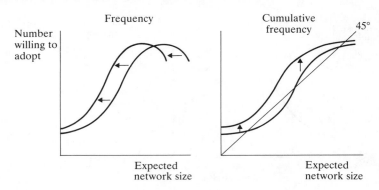

Figure 5.2 Reduction of mean

curve up. This can be done by reducing the mean of the frequency distribution. The second way to improve the prospects for a high market share for the open standard is to alter market expectations and thus move the market past point B so that the natural momentum of adoption takes over again. This involves raising expectations that the network will grow to be large irrespective of the observed adoption of the standard.

Method 1 An upward shift of the cumulative adoption curve requires reducing the mean of the frequency distribution. This, in turn, implies increasing the number of customers who would be willing to join the network for any expected network size (see Fig. 5.2).

This can be achieved by the firms in the open systems group as follows:

1. *Firms can reduce the loss a customer would experience if 'stranded' (i.e. if the network stays small).* Logically, the open standards alliance should segment the market and target the newly developing segments with stand-alone uses. Furthermore, it should promote virtues other than network economies. In this way, the obstacle of the existing installed bases compatible with other standards is minimized, and the value to customers of network economies is smallest. Entering a vacuum, the network will grow, first in stand-alone use where it will coexist with larger network standards. As it reaches sufficient size, it can be migrated into other market segments.

   This is precisely the way by which open standards are developing. UNIX (and technical workstations where UNIX has its strongest position) first appeared in scientific and engineering applications in businesses and universities. Here its virtue of adaptability and flexibility for sophisticated users/programmers was an asset. Departmental computing applications followed. Only now is the market widening to encompass financial analysts, publishers, and—more slowly—large commercial firms' central data processing where proprietary system standards have historically been at their strongest.

2. *Firms can offer upward compatibility with products of an earlier vintage.* Unfortunately, each X/Open member had a different standard to start with, so there is no common installed base with which to be upwardly compatible. The choice of the largest network standard would have been efficient in the sense that the open systems alliance would have had the best start towards building its network, but such a choice would have had major implications for competition among the open standard members. It was for this reason that they chose a 'neutral' UNIX. The problem of multiple standards' installed bases also exists with a strategy of producing gateways to those other installed bases or of financing the conversion required by existing customers.

3. *Firms can give away equipment.* Educational institutions or other market trendsetters are the usual beneficiaries. This is common with microcomputers but obviously less so with more expensive hardware.

4. *Firms can provide a full range of compatible complementary products.* This would raise the value of adoption irrespective of whether others adopted. Unfortunately, this would require shifting the financial burden of creating complementary products from independent firms to the members of the open systems group.

5. *Firms can increase price competition.* Intra-standards competition would guarantee that customers would not be locked into a monopoly supplier if they were to join the open standards network, and this should increase the number of willing adopters for any expected network size. This is, of course, the principal competitive offering of the open standard alliance.

6. *Firms can introduce a new technology with improved functionality.* The optimal time to introduce new standards, which require the conversion of huge installed bases, is when radically improved technology rewards such a costly conversion. Yet that is not the case

155

here. UNIX (and OSI) are not radical improvements over existing proprietary systems that have installed bases. In fact, they do not offer improved functionality at all. So open systems are likely to enter the industry slowly via new installations rather than via the mass conversion of existing installations. The consequence will be much slower network growth than would take place at a time of radical technological change. Unfortunately, such times only appear randomly, and there is no obvious imminent change in technology that would suggest delaying the shift to open systems.

Method 2 The second way to improve the pospects for a high market share for the open standard is to alter market expectations, that is, to raise expectations that the network will grow to be large irrespective of the observed adoption of the standard. Diagrammatically, this implies a movement along the culmulative adoption curve.

There are a number of ways of doing this:

1. *Firms can misrepresent information on the number of actual adopters.* For example, the firms can claim 'sales' that are really only transfers to distributors and increases in inventories. This is often alleged in the industry.

2. *Firms can use government procurement preference to build confidence that the network will grow.* To the extent that the US and European governments specify or otherwise favour open standards—as they do—expectations of a large future network will rise for any existing adoption level. Government procurement has historically been an important determinant of standards setting in the industry as was shown in the instances of COBOL, ASCII, and with the PCMs.

3. *Firms can increase product promotion.* Advertising and other promotional methods are common mechanisms to increase market confidence in the future of a standard. Product pre-announcements are another.[35]

4. *Firms can offer special price discounts only for early adopters.* This should start the bandwagon and may inspire confidence that the network will continue to grow.

5. *Firms can abandon existing proprietary standards.* The X/Open Group members individually and collectively faced a fundamental choice between simultaneously promoting and upgrading both their

existing proprietary standards and UNIX, thus essentially adding one more standard to the existing set, or terminating development and promotion of their proprietary standards and shifting entirely to UNIX.[36]

The preference of all the firms was to hold on to their existing customers with their proprietary standards but to attempt to attract new customers with open standards. Partly, this preference was due to the risk of losing existing customers to other members, including large firms like DEC. In fact, some members worried that a company like DEC, traditionally dedicated to proprietary systems, was only interested in open systems because it offered an easy avenue into the market of the European founders of X/Open. Certainly, X/Open would look attractive to DEC, given the firm's relatively small installed base in Europe that it would have to protect. A second motive to continue developing proprietary systems was that otherwise, existing customers would be forced to bear the cost of converting their files and programs in return for the promise of an open system in return. For many, this would not have been an attractive trade. In any case, no firm could afford to inflict such a cost on its customers.

Yet by sustaining their proprietary systems, the X/Open members undermined the growth of the UNIX network, prompted doubt about the strength of their dedication to open systems, and committed resources to maintaining proprietary systems (running into hundreds of thousands of dollars annually for each firm) that might better have been invested in some of the alternatives suggested above.

COMPETITION BETWEEN THE FIRMS

In principle, an open standards coalition of firms can be built if each firm believes that it is better off within the alliance than outside of it. However, a number of observers believe that in practice an effective open standards coalition will only be possible when it is competitively neutral.[37] That is, the relative as well as the absolute positions of the firms cannot be harmed by open standards. And it is important to emphasize that competitive neutrality implies more than simply equal access to technology. It also implies that the standard must have equal impact on each firm's customer base, on its manufacturing capability, its product strategy, etc.

A second point to emphasize is that although side payments should

157

permit multi-firm standards irrespective of their competitive implications, in practice side payments feature much more commonly in economic journals than in industry. It is because of this that examples of open standards agreements in other industries generally feature arrangements to ensure competitive neutrality rather than compensation for non-neutral competitive impacts.[38] Thus we see that the open standards alliances such as OSF contemplate independent but jointly owned companies chartered to create, own, and exploit standards commercially by licensing members to use the standards.

The competitive response of the dominant firms

With the appearance of open standards in the competitive arena, firms like IBM and DEC with their large network proprietary standards face a novel challenge. Their response will fundamentally affect the prospects for open standards as well as the fortunes of the small firms that launched the movement.

WHAT ARE DOMINANT FIRMS' OPTIONS?

1. *They can strengthen their competitive positions without changing their overall strategies.* For example, the dominant firms can intensify price competition, increase their rate of research and development, and pre-announce future products compatible with their existing installed bases. The objective of these actions would be to deter the entry of the open standard by undermining customer interest or confidence in the growth prospects of the open standard's network.

2. *Firms can abandon their proprietary standards and join the open standard alliance.* Although at their competitive best in a world of proprietary standards, dominant firms may advantageously embrace open systems in specific market segments where their own system standards are relatively weak. This is what IBM has done in minicomputers and workstations, for example, and what DEC is doing to strengthen its presence in Europe.

   In so doing, however, the dominant firms are taking a risk. By adopting open standards where they are relatively weak, the dominant firms are giving the open systems bandwagon a big push precisely where it has slowly begun to gather momentum. With this push, the bandwagon may accelerate, undermining the income from proprietary standards that the dominant firms depend on. Of course, if the dominant firms do not support the movement, they risk either being left behind (the loss of the Air Force contract noted in the case study is indicative of the cost of neglecting open standards), or the movement could be hijacked by AT & T. That is, the large firms have vested interests not only in their proprietary systems but also in the specific open standard that may finally emerge.

It is not surprising that the dominant firms seem to be ambivalent toward open standards. A good example is IBM's strategy in the technical workstation market. In early 1990, IBM introduced a new hardware line, the System/6000, which runs UNIX AIX. The company announced that it intended to combine a commitment to UNIX, low pricing (including large discounts for conversions from competitors' hardware), and state-of-the-art technology to take one-third of the workstation market by 1992.

If IBM succeeds, it will have contained Sun, Hewlett-Packard, and the others' further expansion into the domain of commercial computing that had long been IBM's preserve. But to succeed, IBM must have the applications software for UNIX AIX. And here, IBM faces a dilemma. Unwilling to embrace wholeheartedly the open system movement, the company has kept AIX incompatible with other versions of UNIX—a strategy certain to limit the availability of software from third-party suppliers. IBM has tried to mitigate its handicap by endorsing an independently supplied gateway that allows many of the hundreds of applications originally written for IBM minicomputers to run on its new workstations. And, of course, IBM can hope that OSF will draw more third-party software into the UNIX AIX orbit.

Even in markets where its proprietary standards are strong, IBM has supported open standards. For example, IBM participated in OSI development since 1977 despite the fact that OSI competes with IBM's proprietary communication standard, SNA (Systems Network Architecture). IBM's reasoning regarding OSI seems the same as it is with respect to UNIX. There is a demand for open systems, and IBM has lost some large jobs in Europe (to competitors like DEC and Honeywell) by not offering OSI. So IBM has tried to ensure that it could supply open standards even if reluctantly. In so doing, IBM is behaving just like its smaller rivals who are reluctant to abandon their proprietary systems even as they promote open ones.

3. *Firms can join the open systems alliance and sabotage it from within.* Much as the open standards groups may have preferred to keep IBM

and DEC out, to do so was impossible if the open systems movement were to remain faithful to its goal. More significantly, however, the open systems groups could not prevent IBM from offering open system products even if IBM were not a group member. In fact, in 1986, IBM offered more UNIX System V applications than did all the X/Open members combined.

Once within the open systems movement, the large firms—IBM, DEC, and AT & T—have been responsible for much of the confusion of standards. OSF is the prime example. OSF's ostensible *raison d'etre* is at least superficially understandable given the threat from AT & T. As long as AT & T as a competitor in the industry was separate from UNIX as an operating system, there was little concern. Only when competitive neutrality was threatened did the other users of UNIX revolt to defend the openness of open systems.

Yet at the time of writing, various conspiracy theories circulate about the OSF firms' hidden motives. There is an obvious suspicion that DEC and IBM want to fragment UNIX, slow the momentum of the open systems movement, and thus preserve the lifetime of their proprietary systems. If this were true, AT & T gave them a perfect excuse to do so.[39]

A second conspiracy theory is that IBM has bequeathed OSF a poor version of UNIX. Once the other OSF members become dependent on it, IBM will release a new and improved version that will be kept proprietary.

4. *Firms can open their own proprietary standards to imitation.* This could be done by liberal licensing or by releasing technical specifications that would encourage cloning.[40] This is the strategy that AT & T chose—a strategy that first became clear with its partial acquisition of Sun. Sun has encouraged cloning of its SparcStation in order to establish its microprocessor technology and AT & T's UNIX as standards in workstations to compete with other firms' hardware and software standards. (This is a strategy closer to Matsushita's in VCRs than to IBM's in PCs.)

AT & T's hope was to unify UNIX under its and Sun's leadership. What was unclear was the companies' ultimate objective. Sceptics feared that the two firms would progressively develop advantageous positions *vis-à-vis* competitors who would be denied timely access to new releases of the standard or who would be disadvantaged by decisions that would favour Sun's hardware. These fears were not

160

mollified when AT & T announced that the new version of UNIX would be optimized for Sun's architecture. In addition, AT & T tightened licensing restrictions on its System V. The restrictions included compulsory compliance with AT & T's interface definition and restrictions on a licensee's right to modify the UNIX code. One sceptic complained that, 'Each time AT & T extends UNIX, the purchase agreement for the system gets more restrictive, and they are radically changing their pricing structure too.'[41] There was even a report in June 1988 that AT & T might deny OSF a licence for UNIX or that it might launch an antitrust case against OSF. Neither threat materialized.

The competitive consequences of open systems standards

If the open systems movement is to prove successful, it will necessarily have a significant competitive impact on the industry. Indeed, a measure of its success will be precisely the scale of that impact. The question we will take up here is what the qualitative nature of the impact might be.

First, open systems standards should depress prices as intra-standards competition replaces quasi-monopoly proprietary standards and marginal inter-standards competition. The increased price competition should come in two forms. One, of course, is the competition between system suppliers who for the first time would have direct access to their competitors' traditional customer bases. Another form is the competition of specialist firms in the sub-markets of system peripherals, components, software, and value-added services. Because standardization will unbundle the different activities in the value-added chain, it will permit these specialists (many of whom may be Asian manufacturers) to enter into direct competition with the sellers of systems. And the intensified price competition of systems will result to some extent in the specialists selling to the systems producers what the latter previously made internally. Systems unbundling will expose weaknesses in a firm's activities and prevent the hidden cross-subsidies that perpetuated them.[42] (This is the reason why open standards often provoke conflict within firms, especially between manufacturing on one hand and marketing and finance on the other.)

In general, the changes described above will be most disadvantageous to those firms whose profits were most dependent on historically locked-in customers, to those firms with traditional hegemony over national markets, to full-line vendors, and to high-cost manufacturers. Ironically, these are characteristics that best describe the small European computer manufacturers that started the open systems movement in the first place.

For example, each of the founding members of X/Open was relatively strong in its national market—ICL in the United Kingdom, Siemens in West Germany, etc. When standards become open, national market boundaries will break down, and national customer bases will be exposed to poaching by larger American firms. Unfortunately for the European computer makers, there is evidence that it is their customers who have been most alienated by historical dependence on proprietary standards.[43] This is not surprising, of course, since those standards had the smallest networks. In any case, only if 'Euro-nationalism', residual customer-specific knowledge, and service networks prove powerful competitive factors will the European firms be able to resist pressure from the foreign producers.

Full-line producers will be disadvantaged because in the traditional absence of multi-vendor standards, they were the guarantors of product line and multi-vintage compatibility. This will no longer be the case with multi-vendor standardization.

High-cost manufacturers will naturally be disadvantaged by competition that shifts to price and thus indirectly to production efficiency. By this criterion of advantage or disadvantage, the Japanese should be favoured (unless they continue to be handicapped by Western countries' trade restrictions). Historically, they have suffered in their export markets (although not domestically where they have an 80 per cent market share) from high cost access to IBM's mainframe system software and a relative lack of applications software, both of which would be ameliorated by open systems. Japanese firms may lack distribution channels and service networks in their export markets, but they have strength in semiconductors. With open systems, technological advantage will be shifted to components and away from more dramatic technological differentiation, which compatibility constrains but which was never a Japanese forte anyway.

Market prospects for the Japanese are confused, however, by Fujitsu's and Hitachi's unique success emulating IBM. Because they are so successful in their domestic market, because they are not nearly as successful abroad, and because IBM will undoubtedly continue to support its proprietary standards, the two firms may simply ignore the open systems movement. (More realistically, they may make only a half-hearted pass at it.) This is particularly likely because for Fujitsu and Hitachi to embrace open systems would expose the Japanese market to competitors to whom it is now effectively closed. Ironically, the Japanese producers are the major beneficiaries of the lock that IBM standards have on their domestic market.

In some respects, IBM might be able to profit from the open systems movement as well. True, it has a large captured customer base, and it is a full-line producer. Yet its captured customers have faced the smallest disadvantage from relative network size and risk of being orphaned. They also have benefited from IBM's well-known marketing strength. And perhaps more than any other firm, IBM has the ability—and the experience—to support more than one standard. It can continue to develop its proprietary technologies for its existing customer base and for specialized applications where dedicated technology is necessarily superior to open systems. And at the same time, it can offer open systems to customers insisting on it.

This highlights one of the problems of the open system movement to its instigators. There is no way that the strategy can be kept away from its erstwhile targets. It is impossible to establish open standards as a competitive weapon to confront dominant producers, without at the same time being exposed to counterattack by those producers using the same weapon.

To suggest that the small and particularly the European firms will be disadvantaged by open systems is not to condemn them for foolishness in starting the movement. As was argued above, they had little choice but to try something radical. Head-to-head competition with IBM, retreat to a niche, IBM-compatibility, mergers and rationalization, and the search for relief via antitrust litigation were all tried by one firm or another, and none appeared superior to open systems.

Yet granting the lack of more attractive alternatives, the small producers do indeed face real problems still—problems sufficiently severe that the firms' continued viability cannot be guaranteed irrespective of open systems. The sincerity of their collective commitment to open systems can be questioned. It can be questioned by their continued spending on proprietary systems, by their relative lack of marketing emphasis on open systems, and by their apparent lack of strategic planning for life in a world of open systems. It is surely not evident how the smaller firms will survive when hardware is a commodity (and when much comes from specialist producers), when the operating system is non-proprietary (at least to these firms), and when applications software is supplied by independent vendors (or by IBM, which predicts that it

163

will earn 30 per cent of its revenues from software in the 1990s compared with 13 per cent in 1988).

Is there a more optimistic scenario? If there is, it can be painted as follows. The phenomenon of customer lock-in is perhaps less significant than is commonly believed because most large users have multi-vendor procurement policies.[44] Multi-vendor procurement is practical because large users can integrate their systems with gateways at a cost that, while non-trivial, still is offset by the benefit of freedom from dependence on one vendor.

Because of the prevalence of multi-vendor procurement, price competition is sufficiently intense already that open systems will not lead to much more price competition. Rather, what open systems will do is to lower the users' cost of producing compatibility by substituting multi-vendor standardization for much less efficient gateway technologies.[45] With cheaper production of compatibility, demand for equipment and software may rise dramatically, benefiting all suppliers. The smaller firms will still have to define their competitive advantages, but the challenge to do so in a rapidly growing market with the long-awaited level playing field is less daunting than the pessimistic scenario described above would otherwise suggest.

Conclusions

Unlike the other cases in this book, the story of open system standards in the computer industry is not yet finished. Only when the further passage of time makes the story history will we know what lessons it has for us. Yet there are some observations to make now regarding the background to the movement and a few others to venture as predictions based on the case as presented.

First, IBM has consistently opposed industry-wide standards even though the company has often tempered its opposition by taking part in the various standardization groups. From the COBOL and ASCII experiences of OSI and OSF, one cannot help but see a consistent pattern of behaviour antagonistic to open standards. This would seem to confirm the expectation commonly expressed that dominant firms oppose open standards. And yet there is an obvious ambivalence due partly to the fear of being left behind an open standard bandwagon and partly to a desire to exercise influence on the specifics of any emergent open standard.

Second, this case provides an interesting comparative example of different avenues towards open system standards. In the PC episode of the microcomputer industry, open systems emerged not by plan but as the result of IBM's unexpected loss of its property rights. Once IBM's technology was legally cloned, open standards followed rapidly as a natural consequence of unrestricted access to vendor-supplied hardware and software components that individual micro producers could unilaterally adopt. No explicit coordination between firms was necessary. In the VCR case, the owner of the critical intellectual property chose to capitalize on it by widespread and liberal licensing. In this way, an open standard displaced a competing restricted standard. Here we have a third approach to open standards—one in which property rights are to be renounced in the hope that 'common property' will make common adoption possible.

Will it prove feasible? Will the open system standards movement succeed in the sense of replacing proprietary standards? The prognostication here is pessimistic. To succeed, the members will have to convince users, other industry members, and themselves that they will succeed. Expectations are likely to be self-fulfilling. But this requires a credible and collective commitment to the strategy of open standards—a commitment that seems lacking.

The very concept of open systems in a high-technology industry is likely to prove extraordinarily difficult to implement. There is no evidence that organizational arrangements can be found to offer private firms the incentive to invest in standards for the public domain, nor have public or quasi-public standards bodies been able to *create*, in an efficient and timely way, truly costly and complex technological standards. In fact, the proliferation of *ad hoc* industry groups like SPAG, COS, X/Open, and OSF testifies to industry frustration with the formal standards setting bodies.[46]

To the extent that large firms have joined the bandwagon—a necessary condition for the success of the movement—their participation is suspect. There is no way by which they can be prevented from sabotaging, purposely or incidentally, open systems in their pursuit of competitive advantage. As long as the firms are vertically integrated, so that their creation of technological standards and ownership of property rights to standards can be bundled with hardware and service sales, there will always be the temptation to exclude access to others and to compete on the basis of full systems. We see this in the present ironic situation of two competing and incompatible open standards groups, each dominated by large companies. The prospect of their peaceful merger at the time of writing is distant at best. In the meantime, firms

165

committing to one group or the other risk making the wrong choice and thus risk a costly conversion in the future. Not surprisingly, many potential customers are deferring decisions until a resolution of the impasse occurs.[47]

How might the impasse be settled? A willingness to cooperate is surely the best solution in a social sense. It is hard to believe that a long period of competition between the two camps is beneficial. The competing standards are essentially undifferentiated in any useful way. They are just incompatible. The fact that there is price competition between them seems to be little compensation to users. To quote Robert Herwick, a senior analyst from Hembrecht and Quist, 'Users don't want [competition between UNIX International and OSF]. Software vendors don't want it. It's a stupid battle between Sun, AT & T, and IBM.'[48]

If there is to be competition between the open standards groups, UNIX International has the advantage of being the first mover. It already has products on the market while OSF's are lagging. Yet OSF boasts the greater market share in terms of the positions of its member companies. If the VCR story is any guide, market share is the more important advantage.

Will the small firms that started the movement be saved by it? They will probably find that a strategy of using open standards to compete with large firms' proprietary standards will not work in any clear-cut fashion. The reason is that, by definition, large firms cannot be excluded from joining the movement themselves, possibly as free riders. The more successful the open systems movement is, the more will large firms offer products compatible with the open system specifications. It would be truly ironic if large firms were to seek competitive advantage by mimicking the standards of the small firms. In the end, this may favour open systems, but since it would no longer be the movement of the small firms, it would not necessarily help them. Furthermore, once large firms are within the movement, they will exert their influence on its agenda, and this influence may be destructive to the interests of small firms.

If the open system standards movement fails and competing proprietary standards reaffirm their hegemony in the industry, then compatibility will have to be achieved, if at all, by some means other than multi-firm standardization agreements. Perhaps it will come via the progressive dominance of one firm, perhaps from more successful efforts of clones than has historically been possible, perhaps from more and more gateway production, or perhaps from a renewed attack by public policy bodies. Governments have used their buying power with considerable success in the past, yet they have generally been unsuccessful in using their lawmaking powers to influence the determination of standards. Perhaps they will find again the need to try to influence open standards via the law. If so, the approach used in the regulated US telecommunications industry—requiring arm's-length separation between corporate research and development departments and manufacturing—should be considered.

Notes and references

1. The 'Gang of Nine', discussed in the chapter on microcomputers, is one analogy. Another analogy is the competition between Sony's open 8 mm standard and JVC's proprietary VHS standard discussed in Chapter 3.
2. These standardized high-level programming languages did not make it possible to move programs from one producer's computer to another's. They did make transcribing programs between computer models easier, however, and they were a prerequisite for the development of the IBM-compatibles that came later.
3. The System 360 standard, with modifications, is still the dominant IBM mainframe standard. Newer hardware generally has been able to run software for older machines, although the reverse is sometimes not possible.
4. The principal case was the 1973 *Telex* v. *IBM* that was won by IBM on appeal.
5. Fujitsu took nearly 50 per cent of the company in 1984.
6. Amdahl tried to copy IBM's operating system software, too, but its six-year and $10-million effort failed in 1987.
7. The dozen major producers in the mid-1950s included Monroe Calculating Machine, Underwood, Electrodata, Bendix, Raytheon, and Marchant Calculators, none of which was a major participant a decade later.
8. This is particularly ironic given Honeywell's emulation of IBM's standard with the H-200.
9. Much has been written about IBM's allegedly anticompetitive behaviour, and many writers claim that the company should have been found guilty. See, for example, Adams, W. and J. Brock, Integrated monopoly and market power: System selling, compatibility standards, and market control, *Quarterly Review of Economics and Business*, Winter 1982; Bartkus, R., Innovation competition: beyond *Telex* v. *IBM*, *Stanford Law Review*, 28, January 1976; and Braunstein, Y. and L. White, Setting technical compatibility standards: An economic analysis, *Antitrust Bulletin*, Summer 1985.
10. IBM was alleged to have dominated the market for IBM-compatible machines rather than the broader mainframe computer market. The broader market definition would have included the incompatible computers

167

of Burroughs, ICL, and others and would, of course, have made the case harder for the prosecution to win.

11. Computer systems integration is an important, lucrative, and rapidly expanding segment of the consulting business with $17 000 million of revenues in 1989.
12. *Business Week*, 24 June, 1985.
13. The ISO started work in 1977 to define an architecture for communications among heterogeneous computer systems. Final approval of OSI as an international standard came in 1983. Over the same period, the CCITT was working on a telecommunications reference model, and the two organizations agreed to merge their standards in 1983.
14. Other important open systems groups are SPAG (the Standards Promotion Applications Group) and COS (the Corporation for Open Systems). Both focus on open standards in computer communications. The former is a European organization while the latter is a US organization.
15. Quoted from an X/Open promotional brochure.
16. See Chapter 2 for a discussion of UNIX in the microcomputer market.
17. That decree, part of the settlement of an antitrust case, barred AT & T from the computer industry.
18. In a 1985 survey of large European corporations undertaken by the author, only 2 per cent of respondents named UNIX as their principal data processing standard. Only 19 per cent had any UNIX applications at all.
19. The reason why there were so many different hardware implementations was that UNIX was written in the standard C language (which like UNIX was developed by Bell Laboratories).
20. Quoted in *Datamation*, 15 April, 1986, p.31.
21. Sun was a leading producer of extremely fast desk-top engineering work-stations. Sun's early success (it reached $1000 million in sales six years after its founding) was due to its concentration on standardized software, in particular on UNIX.
22. Fear of OSF's low software prices prompted a group of independent software companies to complain publicly in early 1990 that the hardware firms that dominated OSF were abusing their market power and that OSF was in essence a cartel of hardware firms. One software company threatened litigation but has not yet insituted a case.
23. The threat only receded in 1984 with passage of a law that allowed companies to engage in cooperative research and development without risk of antitrust prosecution.
24. Brock, G., *The U.S. Computer Industry: A study in market power*, Ballinger, Cambridge, Mass., 1975, p.106
25. The strategies suggested here are essentially the same as those available to Sony when Betamax's share of the VCR market started to decline in competition with VHS.
26. Compare Brock, *op.cit.*; Ordover, J. and R. Willig, An economic definition of predation: Pricing and product innovation, *Yale Law Journal*, Novem-

ber 1981; and Katz, M. and C. Shapiro, Network externalities, competition, and compatibility, *American Economic Review*, June 1985.

27. 'Standard' gateway software at the time could convert some programs from IBM's VMS operating system standard to UNIX. To the author's knowledge, however, no such programs were available for the European firms' systems.

28. More recently, some merger activity has started, for example Siemens' acquisition of Nixdorf in 1990.

29. In particular, it could not accommodate multi-tasking and multi-users.

30. See the discussion in Chapter 2.

31. At the time, AT & T was not a member of X/Open. Olivetti, of which AT & T owned 25 per cent, was a member, but it was independent of the managerial influence of AT & T. Still, X/Open members might have been concerned that Olivetti would have a conflict of interest between X/Open's and AT & T's control of the standard.

32. This general point is explored in G. Stigler, The theory of economic regulation, *The Bell Journal of Economics*, Spring 1971, and in S. Peltzman, Towards a more general theory of regulation, *Journal of Law and Economics*, August 1976.

33. The Commission has, for example, supported cooperative research in the area of high-definition television.

34. See Schelling, T. C., *Micromotives and Microbehaviour*, Norton, New York, 1978.

35. See, for example, Farrell, J. and G. Saloner, Installed base and compatibility: innovation, product preannouncements, and predation, *American Economic Review*, December 1986.

36. This is the strategy that IBM used when it ceased production of the PC to stimulate sales of the PS/2. See Chapter 2.

37. Compare Brock, *op.cit.*, and Besen, S. and G. Saloner, Compatibility standards and the market for telecommunications services. In Crandall, R. W. and K. Flamm (eds), *Changing the Rules: Technological change, international competition, and regulation in telecommunications*, The Brookings Institution, Washington DC, 1989.

38. See, for example, the discussion of the 'Gang of Nine' in Chapter 2.

39. It is ironic, of course, that DEC and IBM were the ones to complain about AT & T's prospective licensing policy.

40. This is, of course, what the settlement of the European Commission case against IBM intended to require of the company.

41. Craig Lund of Charles River Data Systems, quoted in *Datamation*, 15 August, 1986, p.30.

42. The process took place at Apple as described in Chapter 2 when Sculley started to purchase Macintosh components that were manufactured in-house under Jobs's leadership.

43. This was one of the findings of the author's survey of computer users cited in note 18 above.

44. A finding of the author's survey of computer users in Europe cited above was that 54 per cent of respondents had multi-vendor procurement policies in their central data processing area.
45. The losers in this scenario will be the independent software and consulting firms whose *raison d'être* is to produce the gateways that now integrate incompatible computer systems.
46. For a discussion of this, see Berg, J. and H. Schummy (eds.), *An Analysis of the Information Technology Standardization Process*, North Holland, Amsterdam, 1990.
47. In an International Data Corp. Survey, 25 per cent of those polled said that they were postponing UNIX purchases.
48. Quoted in the *International Herald Tribune*, 21 June, 1990.

6. Conclusion: A dozen hypotheses about standards and competition

Introduction

The purpose of this concluding chapter is to present some hypotheses regarding standardization and competition, which can be deduced from the cases in the book (and a few other cases to which allusion will be made). These hypotheses are not meant to be 'truths' in the sense that deductions from mathematical models are truths (by tautology) or in the sense that statistical evidence can vouch for the truth. Rather, these hypotheses are offered more modestly as 'tendencies' or 'crude generalizations' for which there may be many exceptions (the most obvious of which will be noted). Although this may be a modest intellectual objective, I believe, as do others,[1] that formulating inductive hypotheses from case observation is crucial to our understanding of the positive and normative aspects of the phenomenon of standardization that intensely concerns business and public policy makers.

The deductive mathematical models, which are appearing more and more in the economics literature (and which are in sharp contrast to what will appear here), provide helpful insights, but their utility is fundamentally limited. Why? In order to be tractable, the structure of the models must necessarily be very simplistic. Individual models may address in a highly stylized way an interesting element of the topic, yet no model can (or purports to try to) capture more than a small piece of a very complex phenomenon, all elements of which are interrelated. Another problem with the theoretical models is that they inevitably give ambiguous results. In other words, a variety of outcomes (often exact opposite outcomes) is always possible. So while the models may be able to classify possible outcomes, they have trouble predicting them. And the intuition that underlies the various possible outcomes, while often interesting, is equally often difficult to comprehend intuitively.

None of this is to imply that deductive modelling has no value, for it does. Both inducing generalizations from specific case observations and deducing specific conclusions from general axioms have strengths and weaknesses as research methodologies. Yet the value of each can be improved when complemented by the other, and that is to be the approach of this chapter. I will accompany each of the hypotheses with reference to whatever formal deductive models are relevant.

Hypothesis 1: Standardization is often not the best way to achieve compatibility

In conducting the research for this book, I was struck by how often people made what I regard as two mistakes in thinking about standardization. One was to believe that standardization and compatibility were synonymous terms. The other was to believe that standardization can be accomplished freely (or at least cheaply). Together, these beliefs lead to the conclusion that standization is invariably desirable. Yet it often is not.

In the first place, and as was discussed in Chapter 1, compatibility is not synonymous with standardization. Compatibility is a relational attribute between products that consumers presumably desire. Consumers want their computer software to be compatible with the hardware, car tyres with their rims, etc. Like the demand for any other good, the demand for compatibility depends upon a number of factors. The size of the user network is one that is peculiar to standards. But in common with the demand for any other good, the demand for compatibility depends on its 'price', and its price in turn depends on its production cost. The more expensive the achievement of compatibility, the less consumers will demand of it, that is, the less of it they will be willing to pay for.

None of this directly implies anything about standardization. Standardization is not synonymous with compatibility but is rather a specific way of *producing* compatibility. Compatibility is produced by designing complementary products in conformance with a common technical specification—the 'standard'. Thus, the demand for standards is derived from the demand for compatibility. But as was described in Chapter 1, there are other ways by which compatibility can be produced—by gateways or conversion technologies in particular—and in some instances they may be superior.

These different ways of producing compatibility are competitors, and we saw a good example of their rivalry in the case of the three standards in camcorders—VHS, VHS-C, and 8 mm. Fully standardized VHS equipment (VCR and camcorder) can be used with no necessary conversion. All is perfectly standardized. (The same is true with Betamax equipment, which still exists in small numbers.) But the VHS

172

format is bulky and cannot match the functionality of a piece of hardware dedicated to videography. Sony's 8 mm format is functionally ideal for videography, but it requires transcription between the incompatible 8 mm and VHS standards. Finally, the VHS-C standard is a compromise functionally (it has a short play time) but there is an inexpensive gateway (an adaptor) to the standard VHS. Ironically, the case of VCRs is often used to illustrate how market competition leads to a universal standard. In fact, it embodies as well a case of competition between standards and gateways.

The example of natural languages used in Chapter 1 and reference to our cases should make it clear that universal standardization is often not optimal. It can be extraordinarily costly to acheive, and consequently it is often preferable to use conversion technologies. This explains why the various ways of producing compatibility often coexist in apparent stability. Language is again an obvious example. Computers and VCRs are others. In none of these cases could a single universal standard ever be described as the industry condition. Of course, part of the reason might be that producers prevented industry-wide standardization. But at the same time, the cost of converting installed bases (e.g. in the case of mainframe computers) would have been extraordinary. Figuratively speaking, if one starts after the Biblical story of the Tower of Babel, gateways are likely to be cost effective in many situations and are often seen. The current proliferation of gateways and multi-standard microcomputers is probably a superior means of achieving compatibility than the imposition of a single standard or the acquiescence of all the producers to just OS/2 or some other operating system. In general, as technology advances compared to the rate of advance of our organizational capabilities, one is likely to find that gateways get progressively cheaper compared to industry-wide standards. If so, one can predict that we will see compatibility produced more and more by gateways.

To carry the argument here one step further, universal compatibility is often not optimal either. Incompatibility will be efficient if its cost is less at the margin than the cost of achieving compatibility.

The various costs and benefits of alternative ways of achieving compatibility are summarized in Fig. 6.1.

Summarizing Fig. 6.1, separate incompatible standards obviate network economies but avoid the cost of converting installed bases if there are any. They also afford variety—an issue to be discussed later. A single universal standard has the reverse costs and benefits. Finally, gateways can offer both network economies (by connecting otherwise

173

	Cost	Benefit
Separate networks	Unexploited network economies	No necessary conversion
Connected networks	The gateway	Network economies and variety
Single universal network	Conversion of installed bases, functionality, and possible variety	Network economies

Figure 6.1 Costs and benefits of alternative ways of producing compatibility

incompatible networks) and variety, but with the obvious cost of producing the gateway. (There may as well be a cost of degraded functionality in going through gateways as we saw repeatedly in the cases.)

The existence of these different ways of producing compatibility is significant for competitive strategy. Because they are alternative ways of satisfying consumers' primary demand for compatibility, they should be thought of as competitors in a market. The firms that custom-produce compatibility between incompatible computers (e.g. the small value-added retailers in the computer networking business) should see the industry movement to open standards as a competitive threat. The firm that is intent on locking customers into a proprietary standard may face competition from the producer of an adaptor (like the software that translates IBM software to UNIX compatibility) that would allow those customers to escape.

Although I believe that this hypothesis is generally valid, I believe none the less that there is too little product standardization.

Hypothesis 2: There is not enough product standardization
One of the most basic questions to ask is whether *laissez faire* markets generate the appropriate amount of compatibility and standardization. Since there are benefits to compatibility that are external to the market, one's expectation might be that an insufficient amount of compatibility will occur naturally. In fact, this was common reasoning before the era of formal modelling,[2] and it was often assumed by modellers who chose not to examine it explicitly.[3]

The intuition is simple enough. Much of the economic benefit of an incremental increase in network size does not accrue to the incremental network member but is shared by all members of the network. For example, as more and more consumers bought VHS equipment and the VHS network grew, it became economical to develop the movie rental business benefiting all network members. Since the consumer's decision to buy into the VHS network is based on personal rather than collective benefits, there is an inadequate incentive for network membership. This problem of market 'externalities' is well understood in economics, and it will normally result in an insufficient registered market demand for compatibility.

Markets may fail to function properly due to externalities on the supply side as well. A standard is intellectual property, and like all intellectual property it is a public good. Once produced, it may be possible for firms that did not support its production to use it at no cost. We saw this problem repeatedly in the cases. If enough firms try to be 'free riders', there will be insufficient investment in standards. Of course, the firms that do invest in standards may try to exclude free riders from using them without paying. This again was commonly observed in the cases. If property rights to standards can be defined and defended (which, as we have seen, is possible to some degree in most cases of technology standards) this will often be the case, but it does not necessarily mitigate the problem of undersupply. Monopoly results in undersupply too as the early history of the computer business demonstrated well. Other institutional mechanisms to overcome the free rider problem seemed in the cases to work poorly, including public standards-setting agencies and voluntary agreements (except in the automobile case where the standards were not patentable).

Katz and Shapiro[4] were perhaps the first researchers to consider explicitly and formally the question of market supply of compatibility. They modelled the demand side external benefits referred to above. On the supply side, they modelled a static oligopoly. They found that the private incentive for compatibility was less than the social incentive, that is, there would be too little compatibility. However, in a subsequent paper[5] the two showed that although there was a bias towards an undersupply of standardization, the opposite and counterintuitive result—an oversupply—was also possible. Excess standardization was most likely to occur when one technology was proprietary and the other was not. The proprietary technology could displace the non-proprietary one even when it was optimal to have both.

175

Other researchers found that too much standardization and compatibility was possible although for different reasons.[6] A common feature of their work was recognition that standardization has social costs as well as benefits. This reiterates the point made in hypothesis 1 above—a point that Katz and Shapiro ignored when they assumed that standardization was free of cost. Once one recognizes explicitly that standardization can be costly, it can readily be demonstrated that a *laissez faire* market can produce too much of it.

Still, despite the caveats, it remains likely—and this conclusion seems to be supported by our cases—that markets face inherent organizational and incentive problems creating standards, and consequently the amount of standardization will generally be inadequate.[7]

Hypothesis 3: Multiple incompatible standards can coexist in a quasi-equilibrium in a market

The best news for those seeking a technical standard is that there are so many to choose from.

A joke among standards-setters

The network economies that characterize standards should lead eventually to a single standard in a market, much as took place in the VCR case with the spread of the VHS standard to the detriment of Betamax. Yet even casual observation should be sufficient to suggest that multiple incompatible standards can coexist for long periods of time in a rough 'quasi-equilibrium'. In the mainframe computer industry, this quasi-equilibrium has existed for as long as the industry itself, even though it may now break down under the pressure of the open standards movement. In the case of natural languages, incompatible 'standards' have coexisted since pre-historic times with little evidence of convergence to commonality.

Not surprisingly, there are numerous explanations for the vitality of competing incompatible standards. One, which to a degree contradicts the statement of the hypothesis, is that the different standards occupy different market segments and thus do not truly compete. Referring to the VCR market again, although VHS is clearly the dominant format today, Betamax machines outnumber VHS by wide margins in some regional markets. The network economies are sufficiently exploited in those geographical areas that little change is now taking place. As an analogy, most people rarely come into contact with any language save their own.

The coexistence of incompatible standards, in what is clearly a single market, often traces its origins to a time when the market was segmented, and the segmentation allowed the different standards to establish installed bases. With the passage of time, demographic, cultural, technological, or other changes eliminated the logic of the segmentation bequeathing a single market several well-entrenched but incompatible standards. From this point, the costs of conversion outweighed the network benefits, and the incompatibility persisted. Examples are easily found. The mainframe computer business is one. Betamax and VHS is another (recognizing that regions exist where Betamax is dominant). The two standards' networks grew before the play of pre-recorded films developed, that is, before there were significant network economies. The Macintosh got its start in desk-top publishing where it was isolated from direct competition with IBM's PC, which served most of the other microcomputer user segments. Over time, the two standards came to serve the same market, but to date the Mac has continued to hold its position. Before the Mac-PC episode, a similar situation arose with the Apple II and the various CP/M machines; the former originally focused on games and the latter on business applications. The obvious implication for strategy is to enter a market segment in which there is a vacuum, build an installed base, and then migrate into a broader market occupied by a competitive standard. This is the apparent strategy of X/Open.

Although one could imagine that eventually both the Betamax and the Macintosh will disappear in competition with standards with much larger networks, the pace of technological change may be sufficiently rapid (especially since the phenomenon of technical standardization is most evident in markets that are technologically dynamic) that convergence never occurs. In the early life of many technologies like VTRs, computers, and automobiles, no semblance of standardization occurred because the technology (and often the consumer's understanding of the product) was not sufficiently mature and stable to allow it. Even now, when the microcomputer market has passed from being a novelty to showing many signs of comparative maturity, new operating system standards such as OS/2 and more recently UNIX have appeared before the prior generation battled to a conclusion.

Another factor that may prevent the convergence of standards is the exhaustion of the network economies short of the full market size. For example, the Macintosh has attracted a sufficiently large market to entice the investment of third-party producers of complementary prod-

177

ucts, which are offered in varieties and at prices roughly comparable to those of IBM and IBM-compatible microcomputers.

Another explanation for the coexistence of incompatible standards is the ability of users to achieve compatibility between alternative standards' networks via gateways. Microsoft's Z-80 card, which allowed Apple IIs to mimic CP/M machines, essentially eliminated the market pressure that would otherwise have threatened the Apple with obsolescence in competition with CP/M's larger network.

Finally, and a point related to the two above, producers of complementary products may be able to make multiple versions for the different standards' networks cheaply. This may be more economical than a gateway, and it reduces the network economies. As an example, software firms commonly transcribe applications programs from one computer operating system standard to another. Microsoft's Excel, available for both the Macintosh and the PC, is a case in point. Similarly, many Macintosh programs are currently being adapted to run on OS/2. As the number of installations of competing standards increases, so does the financial return on the investment of transcribing software applications from one standard to another.

Hypothesis 4: A dominant firm will oppose and weak firms will favour multi-firm standardization (open standards)

To the extent that a firm can capitalize on a standard's network economies to displace other incompatible standards with smaller networks, it may be able to extract the monopoly profit. It will not be in the firm's interest to have that profit dissipated by intra-standards competition. (There is a possible exception which recognizes that a monopolist may profit by second-sourcing its proprietary technology in order to improve its attractiveness to the market. This will be discussed below.)

Numerous researchers are convinced that dominant firms systematically try to obstruct multi-firm standards for just this reason, and IBM is their best corporate case. Standards-specific cases include COBOL, ASCII, the CCITT X-400 electronic mail standards, and OSI.[8] The more recent open standards initiative in computers in this book is another example. These are all instances in which the standard of the dominant firm was proprietary, but this need not be the case. In the period 1910–20, Ford and GM were hostile to the SAE's standardization movement. Industry-wide standardization of parts dimensions and materials 'levelled' the playing field' that had been tilted in favour of the

178

large, vertically integrated firms that had the volume to standardize components internally.

The example of the PC is worth a digression because with it, IBM is intimately associated with open architecture and industry-wide standards in an apparent contradiction of the hypothesis. Yet a closer look gives a different interpretation. When IBM introduced the PC, it was a new entrant and not a dominant firm. Furthermore, its PC strategy was in many respects alien to the company's tradition and more readily attributable to a handful of independent individuals operating outside of IBM's general management influence. Finally, it is disputable that IBM intended the PC to be cloned. Even though the PC was relatively open, it nevertheless embodied proprietary technology that IBM did not intend to be replicated as easily as it was. Perhaps a better test of the hypothesis comes with IBM's PS/2, dubbed the 'clone killer', which IBM undertook from a position of dominance and with the benefit of its experience with the PC. Here we see the hypothesis clearly sustained.

Beyond the inferences of case observations, formal modelling has demonstrated as well that dominant firms will oppose and weak firms favour multi-firm open standards. To quote:

> We find that firms with good reputations or large existing networks will tend to be against compatibility, even when welfare is increased by the move to compatibility. In contrast, firms with small networks or weak reputations will tend to favour product compatibility, even in some cases where the social costs of compatibility outweigh the benefits.[9]

This quotation notes the corollary that weak firms (i.e. firms with small market shares) will favour open standards (subject to some qualifications to be discussed below) as a strategy to break the disadvantage they would otherwise face with a collection of incompatible small network standards. We saw many examples of this strategy in our cases. Sony proposed the open 8 mm standard for VCRs and camcorders after it lost the inter-standards competition with VHS. The open CP/M operating system standard for microcomputers emerged from a set of firms, each of which was weaker than the dominant Apple with its proprietary Apple/DOS. The founders of X/Open, dedicated to open standards in computing, were the small European producers. A final example is the 'Gang of Nine', formed to oppose IBM's proprietary Micro Channel.

This common form of competition is more than just competition between alternative standards. Fundamentally, it is competition between

179

alternative processes by which standards are set—market competition versus cooperative agreement. And the advantages and disadvantages of each process are illuminated in these examples by the harsh light of direct rivalry. One can see what those respective advantages and disadvantages are. Proprietary standards have the distinct advantage of providing the investing company with a return on its investment. The commercial motive is pure. But the disadvantage—the risk of monopoly abuse that a rational customer must be presumed to fear—is also clear.

In contrast, cooperatively set open standards mitigate the monopoly risk by guaranteeing intra-standard competition, and thus they should lead to an expanded market. Not surprisingly, users are generally in the forefront of the open standards initiatives. But open standards have their own special problems, which are of two kinds. One is the problem of free riders. The other is the problem of coordination which itself has two aspects. One is the cost of administration and the other is the problem of resolving what are inevitably diverse technical preferences of the firms in the open standards alliance.

The free rider problem will be serious in any situation in which the standards in question require a costly investment—invariably the case in electronics industries. In fact, the free rider problem is generally so serious that in significant cases of open standards, one finds that the problem was fortuitously avoided rather than solved. The case of the open standards movement in the computer industry today is illustrative. The standards themselves centre on UNIX and OSI—neither of which was developed by the firms in the various open system alliances. It is interesting to imagine how far the open systems movement would have gone had the firms had to create UNIX and OSI *de novo* on their own financial resources. Even in the case of the SAE in the early days of the automobile industry, when standardization was not extraordinarily costly, standardization was financed by the revenues from the historically unique Seldon patent rather than from any cost-sharing agreement among the benefiting firms.

The problem of resolving the inevitable differences arising among the members of an open standards alliance is sufficiently important to deserve separate analysis.

Hypothesis 5: Multi-firm standardization will only be achieved when it is competitively neutral
The corollary to Hypothesis 5 is that multi-firm standardization is most likely in an industry that is not vertically integrated

One of the problems with open standards agreements is that each party must see the alliance serving its interests. In principle, this only requires that each firm believes that it is better off within the alliance than outside it. ('Outside' does not necessarily mean in opposition to the alliance. It could also mean free-riding on the work of the firms that are active members of the alliance.) In practice, however, the condition required to induce a firm's participation is likely to be somewhat more strict. Many academics believe that open standards are only possible when they are competitively neutral.[10] Our cases seem to agree with this belief.

It is important to emphasize that competitive neutrality requires more than non-discriminatory access to technology. It also requires that standardization must have equal impact on each firm's customer base, on its manufacturing capability, etc. The SAE standards for automobile components were equally and freely available to all producers, yet they had competitive implications. The firms in the industry were of different sizes with different degrees of vertical integration. Each started with a different installed base of tools and dies, customers, and design philosophies. Each of these differences implied a competitive asymmetry with the introduction of standards and rendered the process of standardization more difficult than it would otherwise have been. As it turned out, standards had few net competitive implications within the set of small firms, all of which were party to the standardization efforts. The larger firms, which were relatively disadvantaged, were not active participants until after the small firms had ceased to be a competitive threat. As another example, Sony's proposed 8 mm format for VCRs was surely not competitively neutral despite being non-proprietary. Nor was it to be an acceptable industry standard to the firms in the VHS camp.

A second point to emphasize is that in principle, side payments should permit multi-firm standards irrespective of their competitive implications. Yet we see no examples of side payments. Even in the case of VCRs, when MITI offered unknown but surely attractive incentives for either Sony or JVC to abandon its proprietary standard, there was no agreement.

The Sony and JVC example illustrates a related point. Cooperative standards must normally be agreed upon before any significant amount of research and development has occurred. Once a firm's prestige and its managers' careers are intimately connected with a specific technology, it is rare—presuming that the technology has a strong market promise—that negotiations would induce surrender. Another example of inflexible commitment to a technology (one not examined in this book) is colour TV standards.[11]

It is because side payments rarely work that examples of open standards agreements generally feature arrangements to ensure competitive neutrality *ex ante* rather than compensation for non-neutral competitive impacts *ex post*. The EISA standard arrangement, described in Chapter 2, is a good example. And in the computer industry, the founders of X/Open chose to standardize on UNIX, an operating system in which none of them had any initial interest, rather than an operating system belonging to any one of the members. This was not an efficient choice because it cut off *every* firm's installed base, yet it was relatively neutral. (An analogy would be for the European Community to standardize on Japanese or Esperanto rather than on any member's native tongue. Although this may seem silly, the EFTA countries did adopt English as their official language even though none is English speaking!)

There is a corollary to the hypothesis. The corollary is that open standards are most likely in an industry that is not vertically integrated. This point may be disputed[12] because coordination costs between different industries in the value-added chain are surely an obstacle to inter-industry standardization. But others believe as well that vertical separation of the value-added chain helps standardization,[13] and there are many examples showing that the competitive neutrality of a standard set by a vendor can more than outweigh the cost of inter-industry coordination.

The microcomputer industry was one such example. It is significant that the first rough standards in both hardware and software originated with the industry's suppliers rather than with the microcomputer manufacturers themselves. Intel and a few other microprocessor makers provided the core hardware standards. The floppy disk represents another example of a standard that, although introduced by Apple, was not the proprietary creation of the microcomputer makers.

On the software side, since Digital Research and Microsoft did not make computers, they had no motive to restrict access to their operating systems beyond charging a non-discriminatory royalty. Proprietary operating systems do exist in microcomputers, however, and it is worth noting that operating systems have not been as standardized as microprocessors, which are universally purchased.

There are other examples from our cases that can readily be cited as well. Mainframe computer makers are more vertically integrated than micro makers, and their products are less standardized. In VCRs, where the technology arose internally in the industry rather than neutrally from a vendor, standards only came after 10 years of battle. Admittedly, the VCR producers were not originally integrated into software. But in the videodisc business, where competitors like RCA and CBS were integrated into films, there was even less standardization than in VCRs. A similar case is provided by the adoption of 33 r.p.m. phonograph records. This standard was introduced by Columbia, a firm that did not produce phonograph equipment. It made the specifications freely available to all manufacturers to enlist their support for what rapidly became the industry standard. Only the largest vertically integrated producer of equipment and records—RCA Victor—opposed the 33 r.p.m. standard (and tried unsuccessfully to promote 45 r.p.m.).

It is precisely because of the observation noted here that a number of open standards alliances have sought to set up independent but jointly owned companies chartered to create, own, and exploit standards commercially by licensing the shareholders to use the standards. Telecommunications policy to force arm's length separation between a corporation's technology and thus standards-setting activities and its manufacturing business is an analogy.

Hypothesis 6: Standardization will retard the introduction of superior but incompatible technology while increasing the rate of intra-standard technological change

The corollary to Hypothesis 6 is that radical technological change is necessary for the introduction of a new and incompatible standard.

One of the questions that has long attracted the attention of researchers and practitioners is whether standardization retards technological change. Although it is an important and seemingly straightforward question, it is not easily answered.

The question is complicated by the fact that there are a number of dimensions to it. It has a positive dimension: is technological change retarded or not? But there is also a normative dimension, which answers a slightly but importantly different question: does standardization retard technological change *inefficiently*? If a valuable installed base of capital would be rendered obsolete by technological change, it may be wasteful to adopt a 'superior' new technology.

Secondly, one must distinguish between change that entails the replacement of one technology and its related standard by another (i.e. inter-standard technological change) and technological change that

183

occurs within the network of a given standard (i.e. intra-standard technological change). We will find that although standards may well retard the former, they can facilitate the latter.

Finally, one must consider not just the problem of retarded adoption of a superior new technology. One must also consider the possibility that standardization could lead to the adoption of the 'wrong' technology.

We can start with the case of an existing technology and related standard facing the entry of a new and superior yet incompatible technology. (The IBM PC at the threshold of the market dominated at the time by Apple and CP/M machines is an example.)

At an intuitive level, there are several reasons to suspect that technological change of this sort will be hindered, possibly even 'inefficiently'. Most markets are decreasing returns (or negative feedback) systems. That is, the more people there are doing one thing, the less attractive it is for others to do that same thing. For example, the more entry there is into the profession of dentistry, the lower are dentists' incomes, and so fewer young people will want to become dentists. This implies a number of things. Markets will serve diverse customer demands, they will permit small-scale experiments, and they will respond stably to changes in tastes or technology.[14]

Unfortunately, the phenomenon of standardization is not one of diminishing returns. Instead, standards cause positive feedbacks. The more members there are to a given standard's network, the *more* attractive that standard becomes to still others and the larger it will grow. The increasing returns nature of standards has some implications, too. One is that diverse tastes will not normally be served. One or two standards, each serving large numbers of customers, will at best suit what is in some sense a composite need, but minority tastes will be ignored.

Second, and importantly for this discussion of technological change, it is difficult to conduct small-scale market experiments of technological alternatives. A true test must necessarily be on a large scale. This may not have been a significant hurdle in the early life of the industries we studied when standards were in a flux, but it may inhibit innovation and new product introduction in a mature industry with well-established standards. The best and often cited case of a standard blocking the introduction of a better technology is the QWERTY typewriter keyboard, whose letter positions were planned to minimize typing speed so that the old mechanical typewriters' keys would not jam.[15]

The corollary that radical technological change is necessary to introduce successfully a new and incompatible standard was noted by Hemenway who believed that standards were inimical to technological change, and that the best time to introduce a new standard was when the market was in disarray.[16] The logic is that an incompatible new standard will normally require scrapping or converting the old installed base and investing in a new one. To make this attractive, producers must offer clearly superior technology. Since radical technology appears infrequently and randomly, the implication is that competitive opportunities to convert standards are not continuously available but appear with infrequent and unpredictable technological breakthroughs.

We saw numerous examples consistent with this. Each of the microcomputer models that successfully established new standards was technologically radical, or at least novel. IBM's PC introduced the 16-bit chip. Apple's Mac made the jump to the third-generation 32-bit chip. On the other hand, some major failures demanded that users accept incompatibility without the reward of dramatically improved technology. The Apple III and the Rainbow are examples. The PS/2 may ultimately prove to be another since it is not technologically innovative. And if this hypothesis has validity, then X/Open and the other open standards groups will fail, trying as they are to promulgate standards that are not functional improvements over existing and competing standards.

(It should be obvious that radical technology, though a necessary condition for a standards conversion, is not a sufficient condition. The Lisa is an example of radical technology that failed. And as noted above, formal models and the case of QWERTY have shown that even technology to which it is worth converting may not be adopted.)

Although radical technology is usually necessary to introduce a new standard, there are none the less some qualifications.

One qualification to the hypothesis is that very rapid market growth via new customers in a new market segment may facilitate introducing a standard even if it is not dramatically superior. A new and only marginally superior technology could appeal to new entrants in a standards vacuum, while the old technology remained to serve established customers in a mature segment. The entry of 8 mm into the videography market segment, of the Mac in desk-top publishing and of UNIX in departmental computing are all examples from our cases.

Secondly, the hypothesis is less likely to hold to the extent that a new standard does not force rapid conversion of the old. An example

185

illustrates the point. The installed base of the Apple II did not constitute a major obstacle to the introduction of the PC. Why? The reason is partly that the PC was in a different market niche than was the Apple II. And this market niche was growing rapidly. But more significantly, the Apple II was inexpensive to buy and maintain. Thus, it was able to coexist with the PC even in the same household. In other words, the purchase of a PC did not usually require that an Apple II owner convert files and programs to the PC and scrap the Apple II. The Apple II and its software could be kept in the family (usually for the children to play games) despite the investment in a PC and a new base of files and programs.[17]

This is analogous to what one observes with successive generations of audio technologies. Tape cassettes coexisted with the earlier generation of phonograph records. Compact discs were then introduced and coexisted with both earlier technologies. It is not uncommon to find all three kinds of equipment (phonograph turntable, tape cassette player, and compact disc player) in one household. It should be easy for the reader to imagine his or her likely reluctance to adopt a compact disc player if it required that the household library of tapes and phonograph records be immediately scrapped.

In contrast, there are some standards adoptions that require that the old installed base be immediately scrapped. The United Kingdom could never convert to driving on the right little by little. That would necessarily be a revolutionary rather than an evolutionary change. And in mainframe computers, the adoption of a new standard invariably requires a firm to convert completely from the older model and then to scrap it. Running two incompatible systems concurrently for more than a test period is prohibitively expensive.

Finally, and obviously, a new standard that is made compatible with the old, possibly by a gateway, may be adopted with a smaller technological improvement than would be required of an incompatible new standard. And because radical change is less likely to be compatible for technical reasons, firms may often confront a choice between adopting a compatible new vintage of technology with a small improvement in functionality or an incompatible new technology that offers a bigger jump in functionality. This is in essence the choice faced now in the new generation of high definition television (HDTV). The Japanese HDTV technology would require scrapping the entire installed base from broadcasting to the family TV. The European alternative is compatible with much of the installed base, but its quality is not

186

the equal of the Japanese. Neither dominates the other on logical grounds.

A number of economists have looked at the question of standards and technological change using formal deductive models. The first to address the question were Farrell and Saloner. Their conclusion was that markets could exhibit either what they call 'excess inertia' (i.e. they do not convert to a new technology when it is efficient) or 'excess momentum' (i.e. they wrongly abandon the existing technology to adopt a new one that is not worth the conversion costs). Nevertheless, although both outcomes were possible, the researchers clearly regarded excess inertia as the 'standard' case and excess momentum as a theoretical peculiarity.

In their first paper,[18] the two looked only at the supply side and imagined two identical firms facing a sequential decision to offer a new technology on the market. They showed that only under the assumptions of unanimous opinion that the change was desirable and of perfect information would the change be made efficiently. With incomplete information about their respective interests in the new technology, however, the firms' behaviour would always cause excess inertia. This resulted from the fact that it was risky to start the bandwagon of the new standard. The leader might not be followed, and it would then be costly to shift back to the old technology. So neither firm would have a sufficient motive to start the bandwagon even though both wanted the change.

In a second paper,[19] Farrell and Saloner looked at the private and social incentives for consumers to adopt a new technology in a situation in which there was an installed base that was incompatible with the new technology. They found that in this situation, one could observe the efficient outcome, excess inertia, or excess momentum depending in general on what people expected to happen. When a consumer abandons an old technology and adopts the new, he imposes an external cost on users of the old (the network shrinks) and an external benefit on future adopters of the new. These externalities make an efficient outcome unlikely. Whether one gets excess inertia or momentum depends on whether the cost to abandoned users of the old technology is less than, or exceeds, the benefit to the adopters of the new. Instances of excess momentum are hard to prove, but quadraphonic sound and three-dimensional movies are possible examples.

Katz and Shapiro investigated a related question.[20] When the market settles on a standard, will it be the best one or might it be the 'wrong' standard? They built a model of technological change with two incompatible technologies subject to network externalities. But in a departure from the models mentioned above, Katz and Shapiro allowed one or both of the technologies to be proprietary. The authors concluded that a proprietary technology may be adopted over a superior non-proprietary one, and that between two proprietary technologies, the second to be introduced has a strategic advantage and may succeed even if it is inferior to the first. Sony might find grim relevance in this deduction.

The conclusion to which one is led from case observation and these models is that standards surely can and often do retard the introduction of superior new technologies even when their introduction is worth the cost of converting an installed base. The opposite result is theoretically possible, and some examples can be pointed to. But these would be exceptions to the norm.

It would be a mistake to conclude from the previous discussion that standards are deleterious to technological change, however. Inter-standards technological change is only one type. The other is intra-standards technological change, and here standardization is likely to be much more beneficial. In the microcomputer industry, PC standardization stimulated a tremendous amount of technological investment in complementary products, in features like portability, etc.

There are three reasons why intra-standard technological change is likely to be stimulated by standardization. One is that it is an avenue to differentiate an otherwise standardized product. Second, the return on investment in related technology increases as the network's size—and thus the market size—increases. Finally, standardization on a core technology allows innovation to focus on a single element or component of a system without the need to develop an entire new system standard.

Hypothesis 7: The change from an old standard to a new one will not be led by the dominant firm

The cases on microcomputers and VCRs both show a pattern in which successive generations of standards were introduced by firms that failed in the previous generation. Apple, a clear leader with first generation hardware, was succeeded by IBM, which introduced the incompatible second generation 16-bit machines. The shift to the third generation 32-bit machines was again made by Apple. Next, IBM, which eventually lost the PC intra-standards competition, abandoned the PC standard to the victorious clones when it introduced the PS/2. It is ironic that it was the clones that defended what became 'their' standard and opposed the standards conversion away from the PC. In the VCR case, Sony was the one to introduce a successor to the vintage of both VHS and Betamax. The firms selling VHS equipment opposed the introduction. (Interestingly, the allies that Sony found for its 8 mm standard—Kodak and Polaroid—were drawn from the photographic industry, which was a loser to the newer electronic technologies and standards.)

This 'leapfrog' phenomenon appears in some formal models. Farrell and Shapiro assume a situation of overlapping generations of technology.[21] There are two producers and switching costs. The result is a pattern in which the established firm specializes in serving existing locked-in customers at a high price and concedes new customers to the entrant. The entrant, charging a lower price, builds up a base of established customers while the customers of the established firm slowly withdraw or make product-specific investments to escape the lock-in. This eventually reverses the two firms' respective positions. Klemperer has a similar model in which switching costs actually promote an entry cycle.[22] Although switching costs give the established firm a way of blocking entry, they eliminate its motivation to block entry.

All this suggests that standards conversion by technological change is prompted by some combination of a critical mass of abandoned or alienated potential customers and radical new technology. It also suggests the importance of a set of firms outside the main arena of competition that are both willing and able to (re)enter the market through the avenue of radical technological change, rather than by the more expedient but less rewarding strategy of imitation. Interpreted another way, universal industry adoption of one standard is likely to be undesirable for reasons that go beyond what has been discussed previously. It leaves no losers anxious to reverse their fortunes with innovative new products.

Hypothesis 8: Multi-firm standardization disintegrates industries

When system interfaces and peripherals are standardized across producers, new firm entry becomes possible at the level of the individual components rather than only at the level of the full systems. Intra-standards competition will replace inter-standards competition, and all this will force a process of unbundling of system components.

One of the clearest examples of this is in a market we did not study here—the market for consumer audio equipment. The interfaces between different system elements, such as phonograph turntable, tape player, amplifier, speakers, etc., are all standardized so that consumers can and do mix and match components from many vendors. Specialists who compete in the market for only one component, speakers for example, set the price/quality level that the system suppliers must meet for each and every system component.

The consumer audio market is an excellent example of this intra-standards competition, but we saw others in the cases we covered. Parts standardization in the motor industry in its early history increased entry into both parts manufacture and assembly. IBM's System 360 standardization resulted in entry of the PCMs at the component level. IBM's system unbundling was an ultimate result. In microcomputers, standardization around the PC led a myriad of specialists (as well as clone makers) to enter the market. When Sculley opened the architecture of Apple's Mac, he was forced to unbundle its software. Manufacture that was previously performed in-house was subcontracted instead.

When firms are competing within a standard, rents that accrue from the standard itself will be dissipated. Without these rents, and with competition from component specialists, system suppliers will be unable to cross-subsidize specific activities that are not fully efficient (e.g. manufacturing). So a logical consequence of unbundling is a review of make versus buy decisions within a firm, and more frequent buying is a likely outcome. This is the process that leads to increased specialization (of activities in this instance rather than products) and reduced vertical integration. So specialization and low vertical integration are both outcomes of multi-firm standardization as well as causes of it.

In the end, there is little advantage to systems selling once standards allow independent specialists to enter the markets for individual components and customers to mix and match those components. A number of competitive strategies like product tying, the extension of market power from one activity to another (e.g. from minicomputers to microcomputers), price discrimination by metering usage through the demand for complementary products (as in spare parts for cars, and computer tabulation cards) all become impossible. Each and every element of a system must stand on its own merits in a competitive market.

Hypothesis 9: Standardization expands the product market

In general, one would expect standardization to expand a market's size and growth rate. Demand and supply-side externalities are likely to result in too little standardization—a case that was made before—so that increased standardization will be valued by consumers. In the cases we examined, market growth exploded once a degree of standardization appeared (and this in turn reinforced the standards). This was true with automobiles, with VCRs, and with microcomputers. And there is a case to be made, as described in Chapter 5, that the lack of open standards in the broader computer industry has inhibited its recent growth. Surely, no sector in the computer industry is as standardized as microcomputers, and no sector has experienced a penetration rate like it did.

Hypothesis 10: Standardization will reduce the amount of systems variety and increase the amount of component variety on the market
We noted before that the costs of standardization are often underestimated or overlooked entirely by practitioners, and academics are sometimes blind to them as well. Of all the costs or benefits that standardization entails, the change in variety is the least studied and understood.

By definition, standardization reduces the variety of characteristics that are standardized, and this is often its purpose. We saw this clearly in the automobile case. Led by the small automobile assemblers between 1910 and 1920, the Society of Automobile Engineers reduced the numbers of different dimensions and materials of fasteners, spark plugs, wheels, flanges, pipes and tubes, etc., with immense cost savings for these small-volume buyers. But there were undoubtedly some offsetting losses from fewer component shapes, sizes, and materials from which the design engineers could choose. Perhaps these were insignificant, but those involved in the standardization process were sensitive to the risk. Had standardization been carried too far, the cost of reduced variety might have been significant just as it was before the Model T's market dominance was broken by the variety offered by Buick, Studebaker, and Willys. In the farm equipment industry, which we did not examine, a similar process of standardization in the 1920s, to reduce the number of tractor implements, was attacked by the Federal Trade Commission as anticompetitive, and one of the Commission's arguments was that standardization was excessively costly in terms of lost variety.[23]

In general, there will be some trade-off between the economic efficiency of standardization and the value of variety. Will a market strike the appropriate balance? Farrell and Saloner built a simple model of two buyers and two incompatible standards.[24] The buyers had preferences for different standards, yet a single standard yielded network efficiency. The authors showed that there was a tendency for too

191

little standardization, that is, one normally found both standards coexisting when one or the other was optimal. The intuition is that each buyer tried to force an external diseconomy on the other by insisting on its preferred product. Surprisingly, however, too much compatibility was also possible. A single standard could occur when two coexisting but incompatible standards were optimal. This outcome was most likely to occur when the consumers' initially similar preferences diverged over time. This illustrates the point made earlier that history is important in understanding standardization.

Unfortunately, the model by Farrell and Saloner neglects a key aspect of the question. Standardization reduces the variety of characteristics that are standardized, but there may be an offsetting increase in another type of variety. A simple example, drawn from the case of microcomputers, illustrates the point. Standardization on the technology of the IBM PC and MS/DOS reduced the variety of hardware and operating system software on the market. There was perhaps some cost associated with this reduction in variety. But the variety of applications software, peripheral products, and mix and match options for PC owners increased enormously due to the investment of a multitude of independent firms that was made profitable because the standard increased the size of the network. In general, increased standardization and the associated increase in average network size will make it economical for producers to create a greater variety of complementary products.

So there is now a second trade-off. Standardization will normally reduce *systems variety* but at the same time it will increase *complement variety*—the variety of a system's complementary products.[25] The optimal amount of standardization, then, depends on consumers' preferences for two different types of variety as well as on network economies. Do consumers have specialized demands for a variety of basic but incompatible system technologies or do they only care for a large portfolio of complementary products from which to choose, irrespective of the basic system technology? These alternative forms of demand are shown in Fig. 6.2.

Fig. 6.2 illustrates the relationship between the type of variety consumers demand and the type of standard the market may offer. If consumers have a demand for systems variety (demand that often arises because there are many different uses to which the product is put), multiple incompatible standards are feasible if the different standards are able to appeal to the segmentable market. If, by contrast, consumers want a variety of complements, then a structure of incompatible

192

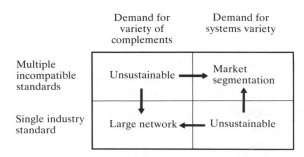

Figure 6.2 Standards and variety

standards is unsustainable, and natural monopoly forces would tend to weed out all but one (subject to the points made in Hypothesis 3).

If consumers want systems variety but are offered a single industry standard, albeit with a large portfolio of complements, again one may have an unsustainable situation. It will be to one firm's advantage to segment the market with a standard specialized to the need of the market segment least well served by the existing standard.

Each of the cells in Fig. 6.2 appeared in one or another of the cases. With VCRs, customers wanted a large portfolio of videotapes (the complements) and cared little for Sony's feeble efforts to differentiate its system from the larger network VHS. So multiple incompatible standards could not coexist (at least not in one geographical market) and were reduced to one (VHS).

Unlike the competition between Betamax and VHS, that between VCRs (in general) and videodiscs did entail sharply different technologies that it was hoped would appeal to different market segments. Videodiscs were specialized for pre-recorded films, and they were superior to VCRs for that use. Hardware and software costs were lower, quality was superior, and producers had copyrights to films. VCRs were general purpose. How would the consumers' demand be manifest? It turned out that CBS and RCA could not segment the market by specialized demand sufficiently to sustain these different technologies. Sony's 8 mm faces the same challenge now. Will there be sufficient specialized demand for videography or will demand for a large portfolio of complements swamp it?

In the earlier history of the VTR, Ampex's VR-7000 failed because the company tried to push a single standard (one-inch tape) on to two market segments—the professional segment and the home user. Unfortunately for Ampex, the market wanted systems variety and had little use for a large variety of complements shared among the different market segments.

The Mac was a success, even though it competed in a market with a strong demand for a variety of complements, because it successfully differentiated itelf to serve a segment that valued systems variety. Its graphics appealed specifically to desk-top publishing and more generally to users who wanted to work in an icon-based environment. The Mac had a small portfolio of complements, but there was sufficient specialized demand for the Mac's technology to outweigh that limitation and to allow the Mac to survive competition from the PC and its clones.

Hypothesis 11: Multi-firm standardization increases price competition

Intuition is probably sufficient to convince most people that multi-firm standardization increases price competition by transforming differentiated and segmented product markets into commodity markets where price competition is in general relatively intense. The story of the cloning of IBM's PC is commonly cited as illustrative of the process. Hardware and software standardization effectively eliminated product differentiation as a competitive tool, it facilitated the entry of new competitors, and it redirected competitive forces to price.[26] Large-scale empirical studies confirm the intuition.[27]

Yet there may be situations in which multi-firm standardization could reduce rather than intensify price competition. A price reduction for one component of a compatible system will raise the demand for complementary components. If different firms' product lines are compatible with each other, any firm that cuts price will find that some of the increase in demand for the complements goes to other firms. This external benefit of a price reduction can be shown to result in less incentive for firms to compete on price than if their products were incompatible and each reaped the full benefit of a price reduction in higher component sales.[28] The formal demonstration of this result requires a variety of preconditions, some readily imaginable and some not. Yet it has been suggested that the farm equipment industry has evidenced the behaviour described.[29]

Despite this possible exception, one would have to conclude that as a stable structural condition, multi-firm standardization should generally imply intense price competition. But this is only one aspect of the issue. The other concerns the dynamic process of competition to set a standard in the market. As we will see, competition between several incompatible standards to establish a monopoly can lead temporarily to very low prices, contradicting the hypothesis.

As was described previously, network economies make markets dominated by standards into natural monopoly markets. As is the case in analogous situations of natural monopoly caused by traditional production economies of scale or learning economies, each producer has a motive to cut price and thus to increase its standard's market share early in the product life cycle in order to establish a monopoly in the end game. Thus, one would expect to see an evolution from multiple incompatible standards and prices below those of an open standard towards a single monopoly standard and a price exceeding that of open standards.[30] Competition to establish a colour TV standard is an example.[31]

The early price competition between firms with incompatible standards may be so intense that it dissipates the reward for the eventual monopolist. (The process is similar to that of bidding for a monopoly franchise.) Indeed, the firms can be worse off than in a comparable market without any customer lock-in at all.[32] This leads one to suspect that in order to avoid this 'destructive' initial competition, rival firms may consciously choose to offer compatible product lines in the first place, either by collaborative design work or by licensing. Once rivals have compatible product lines, a price cut by one of them expands a network that is now common to both. That is, some of the benefit of a lower price is external to the firm offering it. It just gives the rival firm a free ride. This externality will reduce each firm's incentive to cut price. Essentially, the competitors have a motive to choose intra-standard competition over inter-standards competition because in relative terms, the former postpones the competition. This intuitive argument can be demonstrated formally.[33]

There are other reasons as well to expect that suppliers might willingly accept, or even encourage, a single multi-firm standard with some intra-standard price competition, rather than suffer the more intense price competition that could occur between incompatible technologies early in their lives. If one believes that potential customers foresee how vulnerable they will become once locked into a proprietary standard, it is reasonable to expect that their demand will be depressed unless they are given a guarantee that their vulnerability will not be exploited. But how can a supplier make such a commitment? One way is to license other firms so that future intra-standards competition is guaranteed.[34] The widespread practice of licensing second sources of supply in the microchip industry is illustrative.[35] Less explicit (and possibly less conscious) was IBM's decision to open the PC's design to such a degree that widespread cloning could be expected. IBM's decision to encourage other producers to enter the PS/2 bandwagon was more explicit.

We saw some of this played out in the competition between the VHS and Beta standards in the videocassette industry. Rival firms chose incompatible standards in a market that was clearly destined to converge to a single standard. The end-game is now characterized by that single standard (at least in the major national markets), yet it is not monopolistically priced. One of Matsushita's strategies to win the competition with Sony was widespread and low-cost licensing, guaranteeing competition between different suppliers within the VHS network. Evidence suggests that Matsushita's motive was to expand production and disribution rather than explicitly to commit itself to lower future prices, yet the plethora of competitors offering the VHS standard has undoubtedly prevented monopoly abuse. Furthermore, by building market share in this way rather than by a destructive price war, Matsushita and the VCR industry in general were not subject to financial losses.

In conclusion, there are some circumstances in which competing incompatible standards may mean lower prices than those implied by a single multi-firm standard. Yet in the clearest case, this will only be temporary, and there are reasons to expect that firms will look for strategies to avoid even this temporary price rivalry. Such strategies do exist.

Hypothesis 12: Multi-firm standardization will reduce industry profits
Theoretical models have reached this conclusion via two different approaches. Some models[36] argue that intense competition early in a product's life to become the eventual monopoly standard will offset end-game monopoly profits. Other models[37] reverse the timing of cash inflows and outflows. They argue that the best way to promulgate a standard is to commit *ex ante* to allowing eventual competition within it. (The VCR case witnessed both.) So profits are best taken early in the product's life rather than at the end. This is what IBM did with its PC. But regardless of the timing, the same trade-off appears.

By implication, a firm in an industry in which standards are a principal competitive issue needs two distinct but related strategies. One is to establish a standard and the other is to exploit it profitably. Some combination of the two objectives is possible, but it is exceedingly difficult to achieve both in high degree. IBM succeeded in establishing the PC standard with a strategy of open architecture. In the first few years, it profited from its success. Over time, however, the strategy that so successfully established the standard ensured that IBM's profits would erode as clones took advantage of the PC's openness. With the PS/2, IBM seems to be again in a conundrum. The strategy it undertook to profit from the new standard threatened its adoption by others, and strategies it now faces to encourage adoption of the standard threaten IBM's profits from it. Apple, by contrast, never established a standard as dominant as the PC's, yet it profited from the small network it monopolized.

Notes and references

1. Compare Besen, S. and L. Johnson, *Compatibility Standards, Competition, and Innovation in the Broadcasting Industry*, Rand, Santa Monica, 1986.
2. See, for example, Dybvig, P. and C. Spatt, Adoption externalities as public goods, *Journal of Public Economics*, 20, 1983; Kindelberger, C., Standards as public, collective and private goods, *Kyklos*, 36 (3), 1983; and Lecraw, D., Some economic effects of standards, *Applied Economics*, August 1984.
3. See, for example, Besen, S. and G. Saloner, Compatibility standards and the market for telecommunications services. In Crandall, R. W. and K. Flamm (eds), *Changing the Rules: Technological change, international competition, and regulation in telecommunications*, The Brookings Institution, Washington DC, 1989.
4. Katz, M. and C. Shapiro, Network externalities, competition, and compatibility, *American Economic Review*, June 1985.
5. Katz, M. and C. Shapiro, Technology adoption in the presence of network externalities, *Journal of Political Economy*, 94 (4), 1986.
6. Berg, S., Duopoly compatibility standards with partial cooperation and Stackelberg leadership, unpublished manuscript, 1984, and Farrell, J. and G. Saloner, Standardization and variety, *Economic Letters*, 20, 1986.
7. Given this conclusion, one might want the government to compel standardization using legal authority. In the US Senate, the Voluntary Standards and Accreditation Act of 1977 was proposed to establish a National Management Standards Board to manage and coordinate all standards setting activities and to provide a single set of standards recognized by the public and private sectors. And in 1978, the Federal Trade Commission actively sought authority over standards writing and certification. Neither initiative was successful, and in general one does not observe governments legally compelling adoption of particular standards. Governments will sometimes use their power as large buyers, but this is quite different from

using statutory authority to set standards. Thus, our concern here is only with market processes.

8. Brock, G., Competition, standards and self-regulation in the computer industry. In Caves, R. E. and M. J. Roberts (eds), *Regulating the Product Quality and Variety*, Ballinger, Cambridge, Mass., 1975.

9. The quotation is from Katz and Shapiro, *American Economic Review, op. cit.* Ordover and Willig come to the same conclusion in An economic definition of predation: Pricing and product innovation, *Yale Law Journal*, November 1981.

10. Brock, *op. cit.*, and Besen and Saloner, *op. cit.*

11. Crane, R., *The Politics of International Standards: France and the color TV war*, Ablex Publishing Co., Norwood, N.J., 1979.

12. Hemenway, for example, argued that vertical integration would facilitate standardization. See Hemenway, D., *Industrywide Voluntary Product Standards*, Ballinger, Cambridge, Mass., 1975.

13. Compare Link, A., Market structure and voluntary product standards, *Applied Economics*, June 1983.

14. For a development of this argument in more detail, see Farrell, J., The economics of standardization: A guide for non-economists. In Berg and Schummy (eds), *An Analysis of the Information Technology Standardization Process*, North Holland, Amsterdam, 1990.

15. David, P., Clio and the economics of QWERTY, *American Economic Review*, May 1985.

16. Hemenway, *op. cit.*

17. This point about evolutionary versus revolutionary change on the consumer side has a parallel on the producer side. When a producer introduces a new technology and standard, should (can) it continue to offer the old standard? This question faced IBM with its PS/2 as we saw in the case.

18. Farrell, J. and G. Saloner, Standardization, compatibility and innovation, *Rand Journal of Economics*, Spring 1985.

19. Farrell, J. and G. Saloner, Installed base and compatibility: Innovation, product preannouncements, and predation, *American Economic Review*, December 1986.

20. Katz and Shapiro, *Journal of Political Economy, op. cit.*

21. Farrell, J. and C. Shapiro, Dynamic competition with switching costs, *Rand Journal of Economics*, Spring 1988.

22. Klemperer, P., Entry deterrence in markets with consumer switching costs, *Supplement to the Economic Journal*, 1987.

23. Kudrle, R. T., Regulation and self-regulation in the farm machinery industry. In Caves, R. E. and M. J. Roberts (eds), *Regulating the Product Quality and Variety*, Ballinger, Cambridge, Mass., 1975.

24. Farrell, J. and G. Saloner, Standardization and variety, *Economic Letters*, 20, 1986.

25. Braunstein and White made the same distinction in types of variety that is made here. They use the terms 'specialized' and 'portfolio' variety. See

Braunstein, Y. and L. White, Setting technical compatibility standards: An economic analysis, *Antitrust Bulletin*, Summer 1985. Matutes and Regibeau also look at this issue in Mix and match: Product compatibility without network externalities, *Rand Journal of Economics*, Summer 1988.

26. Hergert, M., Technical standards and competition in the microcomputer industry. In Gabel, L. (ed.), *Product Standardization and Competitive Strategy*, North Holland, Amsterdam, 1987.

27. Lecraw, D., Some economic effects of standards, *Applied Economics*, August 1984.

28. Matutes, C. and P. Regibeau, Standardization in multi-component industries. In Gabel, L. (ed.), *Product Standardization and Competitive Strategy*, North Holland, Amsterdam, 1987.

29. Matutes and Regibeau, *op. cit.*; Kudrle, *op. cit.*

30. Klemperer, P., Markets with consumer switching costs, *Quarterly Journal of Economics*, May 1987.

31. Crane, *op. cit.*

32. Klemperer, *op. cit.*

33. Katz, M. and C. Shapiro, Product compatibility choice in a market with technological progress, *Supplement to the Oxford Economic Papers*, November 1986.

34. Farrell, J. and N. Gallini, Second-sourcing as a commitment: Monopoly incentives to attract competition, *Quarterly Journal of Economics*, November 1988.

35. Swann, G., Industry standard microprocessors and the strategy of second-source supply. In Gabel, L. (ed.), *Product Standardization and Competitive Strategy*, North Holland, Amsterdam, 1987.

36. Klemperer, *op. cit.* See also Klemperer, Welfare effects of entry into markets with switching costs, *Journal of Industrial Economics*, December 1988, and The competitiveness of markets with switching costs, *Rand Journal of Economics*, Spring 1987.

37. Farrell and Gallini, *op. cit.*

References and bibliography

Adams, C. A., Industrial standardization, *Annals of the American Academy of Political and Social Science*, **LXXXII**, 1919.

Adams, W. and J. Brock, Integrated monopoly and market power: System selling, compatibility standards, and market control, *Quarterly Review of Economics and Business*, Winter 1982.

Anderson, K., Note on the microcomputer software industry, unpublished case study, Harvard University, 1985.

Arthur, W. B., Competing technologies and economic prediction, *Options*, April 1984.

Arthur, W. B., Competing technologies, increasing returns, and lock-in by historical events, *Economic Journal*, March 1989.

Arthur, W. B., Positive feedbacks in the economy, *Scientific American*, February 1990.

Ashton, P., Some economic effects of standards: Comment, *Applied Economics*, **19**, 1987.

Bartkus, R., Innovation competition: beyond *Telex* v. *IBM*, *Stanford Law Review*, **28**, January 1976.

Berg, J. and H. Schummy (eds), *An Analysis of the Information Technology Standardization Process*, North Holland, Amsterdam, 1990.

Berg, S., Duopoly compatibility standards with partial cooperation and Stackelberg leadership, unpublished manuscript, 1984.

Berg, S., Issues in the determination of compatibility standards: The FCC and AM stereo, unpublished manuscript, 1985.

Berg, S., Technological externalities and a theory of technical compatibility standards, unpublished manuscript, 1985.

Berg, S., Public policy and corporate strategies in the AM stereo market. In Gabel, L. (ed.), *Product Standardization and Competitive Strategy*, North Holland, Amsterdam, 1987.

Besen, S. and L. Johnson, *Compatibility Standards, Competition, and Innovation in the Broadcasting Industry*, Rand, Santa Monica, 1986.

Besen, S. and G. Saloner, Compatibility standards and the market for telecommunications services. In Crandall, R. W. and K. Flamm (eds), *Changing the Rules: Technological change, international competition, and regulation in telecommunications*, The Brookings Institution, Washington DC, 1989.

Bongers, C., *Standardization: Mathematical Methods in Assortment Determination*, Nijhoff, Boston, 1980.

Bongers, C., Optimal size selection in standardization: A case study, *Journal of the Operations Research Society*, 33, 1982.

Braunstein, Y. and L. White, Setting technical compatibility standards: An economic analysis, *Antitrust Bulletin*, Summer 1985.

Brock, G., Competition, standards and self-regulation in the computer industry. In Caves, R. E. and M. J. Roberts (eds), *Regulating the Product Quality and Variety*, Ballinger, Cambridge, Mass., 1975.

Brock, G., *The U.S. Computer Industry: A study in market power*, Ballinger, Cambridge, Mass., 1975.

Brown, A. W., The campaign for high definition television: A case study in triad power, *Euro-Asia Business Review*, April 1987.

Browne, R. and M. Hergert, NEC corporation, unpublished INSEAD case study, 1985.

Burtz, L. and E. Hummell, Standard setting in international telecommunications, *Telecommunications Policy*, March 1984.

Carlton, D. and J. M. Klamer, The need for coordination among firms, with special reference to network industries, *University of Chicago Law Review*, 50, Spring 1983.

Coffin, H. E., S.A.E. succeeds mechanical branch of A.L.A.M., *Automobile*, XXII, 1910.

Collins, H., Conflict and cooperation in the establishment of telecommunications and data communications standards in Europe. In Gabel, L. (ed.), *Product Standardization and Competitive Strategy*, North Holland, Amsterdam, 1987.

Conner, K. and R. Rumelt, Software piracy, unpublished manuscript, University of Pennsylvania, 1989.

Cool, K. and L. Gabel, Standardization and competition in European high technology industries: The case of the European mainframe computer industry. In Cool, K., D. Neven and I. Walter (eds), *European Industrial Restructuring in the 1990s*, Macmillan, London, forthcoming.

Cowan, R., Nuclear power reactors: A study in technological lock in, unpublished New York University working paper, 1988.

Cowan, R., Backing the wrong horse: Sequential choice among technologies of unknown merit, unpublished New York University working paper, 1989.

Crandall, R., Vertical integration and the market for repair parts in the

United States automobile industry, *Journal of Industrial Economics*, July 1968.

Crane, R., *The Politics of International Standards: France and the color TV war*, Ablex Publishing Co., Norwood, N. J., 1979.

David, P., Clio and the economics of QWERTY, *American Economic Review*, May 1985.

David, P. and S. Greenstein, The economics of compatibility standards: An introduction to recent research, unpublished manuscript, Stanford University, 1990.

deLamarter, R. T., *Big Blue: IBM's use and abuse of power*, Dodd, Mead and Company, 1986.

Dybvig, P. and C. Spatt, Adoption externalities as public goods, *Journal of Public Economics*, 20, 1983.

Easterbrook, F., Predatory strategies and counterstrategies, *University of Chicago Law Review*, 48, 1981.

Epstein, R. C., *The Automobile Industry*. Shaw, Chicago, 1928.

Farrell, J., Cheap talk, coordination, and entry, *Rand Journal of Economics*, Spring 1987.

Farrell, J., The economics of standardization: A guide for non-economists. In Berg, J. and H. Schummy (eds), *An Analysis of the Information Technology Standardization Process*, North Holland, Amsterdam, 1990.

Farrell, J. and N. Gallini, Second-sourcing as a commitment: Monopoly incentives to attract competition, *Quarterly Journal of Economics*, November 1988.

Farrell, J. and G. Saloner, Standardization, compatibility and innovation, *Rand Journal of Economics*, Spring 1985.

Farrell, J. and G. Saloner, Economic issues in standardization. In Miller, J. (ed.), *Telecommunications and Equity: Policy research issues*. North Holland, Amsterdam, 1986.

Farrell, J. and G. Saloner, Installed base and compatibility: Innovation, product preannouncements, and predation, *American Economic Review*, December 1986.

Farrell, J. and G. Saloner, Standardization and variety, *Economic Letters*, 20, 1986.

Farrell, J. and G. Saloner, Competition, compatibility and standards: The economics of horses, penguins and lemmings. In Gabel, L. (ed.), *Product Standardization and Competitive Strategy*, North Holland, Amsterdam, 1987.

Farrell, J. and G. Saloner, Coordination through committees and markets, *Rand Journal of Economics*, Summer 1988.

Farrell, J. and C. Shapiro, Dynamic competition with switching costs, *Rand Journal of Economics*, Spring 1988.

Fisher, F., J. McGowan and J. Greenwood, *Folded, Spindled and Mutilated: Economic Analysis and US v. IBM,* MIT Press, Cambridge, Mass., 1983.

Fisher, F., J. McKie and M. Mancke, *IBM and the US Data Processing Industry: An Economic History,* Praeger, New York, 1983.

Flamm, K., *Creating the Computer: Government, industry, and high technology,* The Brookings Institution, Washington DC, 1988.

Ford, H., *My Life and Work,* Doubleday, New York, 1923.

Gabel, L., Product standards and competitive strategy: An analysis of the principles, INSEAD working paper, 1987.

Gabel, L., Open standards in the European Computer Industry: The case of X/OPEN. In Gabel, L. (ed.), *Product Standardization and Competitive Strategy,* North Holland, Amsterdam, 1987.

Gabel, L., (ed.), *Product Standardization and Competitive Strategy.* North Holland, Amsterdam, 1987.

Gallini, N. and L. Karp, Sales and consumer lock-in, *Economica,* August 1989.

Grindley, P., Standards and the open systems revolution in the computer industry, unpublished London Business School Case Study.

Grindley, P., Standards in the VCR Industry, unpublished London Business School Case Study.

Grindley, P., Industry standards and business strategy: An introduction, unpublished London Business School manuscript, 1987.

Grindley, P., and R. McBryde, Standards strategy for personal computers. In Berg, J. and H. Schummy (eds), *An Analysis of the Information Technology Standardization Process,* North Holland, Amsterdam, 1990.

Grindley, P., and R. McBryde, Using product standards and business strategy: The case of video cassette recorders, unpublished manuscript, London Business School, 1989.

Hariharan, S., Technological compatibility, standards and global competition: The dynamics of industry evolution and competitive strategies, unpublished Ph.D. dissertation, University of Michigan, 1990.

Heldt, P. M., The S.A.E. at twenty-five, *Automobile Industries,* **LXII,** 1930.

Hemenway, D., *Industrywide Voluntary Product Standards*, Ballinger, Cambridge, Mass., 1975.

Hergert, M., Technical standards and competition in the microcomputer industry. In Gabel, L. (ed.), *Product Standardization and Competitive Strategy*, North Holland, Amsterdam, 1987.

Hunt, M., Trade associations and self-regulation: Major home appliances. In Caves, R. E. and M. J. Roberts (eds), *Regulating the Product Quality and Variety*, Ballinger, Cambridge, Mass., 1975.

Industrial Standardization, National Industrial Conference Board, New York 1929.

Katz, M. and C. Shapiro, Network externalities, competition and compatibility, *American Economic Review*, June 1985.

Katz, M. and C. Shapiro, Product compatibility choice in a market with technological progress, *Supplement to the Oxford Economic Papers*, November 1986.

Katz, M. and C. Shapiro, Technology adoption in the presence of network externalities, *Journal of Political Economy*, **94** (4), 1986.

Kindelberger, C., Standards as public, collective and private goods, *Kyklos*, **36** (3), 1983.

Klemperer, P., The competitiveness of markets with switching costs, *Rand Journal of Economics*, Spring 1987.

Klemperer, P., Markets with consumer switching costs, *Quarterly Journal of Economics*, May 1987.

Klemperer, P., Entry deterrence in markets with consumer switching costs, *Supplement to the Economic Journal*, 1987.

Klemperer, P., Welfare effects of entry into markets with switching costs, *Journal of Industrial Economics*, December 1988.

Kudrle, R. T., Regulation and self-regulation in the farm machinery industry. In Caves, R. E. and M. J. Roberts (eds), *Regulating the Product Quality and Variety*, Ballinger, Cambridge, Mass., 1975.

Lanzillotti, R. F., The automobile industry. In Adams, W. (ed.), *The Structure of American Industry*, Macmillan, New York, 1971.

Lardner, J., *Fast Forward*, Norton, New York, 1987.

Lecraw, D., Some economic effects of standards, *Applied Economics*, August 1984.

Lifchus, I. M., Standards and innovation: The hidden synergy, unpublished manuscript.

Link, A., Market structure and voluntary product standards, *Applied Economics*, June 1983.

Link, A. and G. Tassey, The impact of standards on technology-based industries: The case of numerically controlled machine tools in automated batch manufacturing. In Gabel, L. (ed.), *Product Standardization and Competitive Strategy*, North Holland, Amsterdam, 1987.

Luce, D. and H. Raiffa, *Games and Decisions*. Wiley, New York, 1957.

Matutes, C. and P. Regibeau, Standardization in multi-component industries. In Gabel, L. (ed.), *Product Standardization and Competitive Strategy*, North Holland, Amsterdam, 1987.

Matutes, C. and P. Regibeau, Mix and match: Product compatibility without network externalities, *Rand Journal of Economics*, Summer 1988.

Matutes, C. and P. Regibeau, Standardization across markets and entry, *Journal of Industrial Economics*, June 1989.

Monteverde, K. and D. Teece, Supplier switching costs and vertical integration in the automobile industry, *The Bell Journal of Economics*, Spring 1982.

Nesmith, A., A long, arduous march toward standardization, *Smithsonian*, March 1985.

Ordover J. and R. Willig, An economic definition of predation: Pricing and product innovation, *Yale Law Journal*, November 1981.

Pava, C., John Sculley at Apple Computer, unpublished case study, Harvard University, 1985.

Pava, C., Note on the history of the U.S. microcomputer industry, unpublished case study, Harvard University, 1985.

Pelkmans, J. and R. Beuter, Standardization and competitiveness: Private and public strategies in the EC color TV industry. In Gabel, L. (ed.), *Product Standardization and Competitive Strategy*, North Holland, Amsterdam, 1987.

Peltzman, S., Towards a more general theory of regulation, *Journal of Law and Economics*, August 1976.

Phillips, A., The role of standardization in shared bank card systems. In Gabel, L. (ed.), *Product Standardization and Competitive Strategy*, North Holland, Amsterdam, 1987.

Postrel, S., Bandwagons and the coordination of standardized behavior, unpublished manuscript, UCLA, 1988.

Postrel, S., Competing networks and proprietary standards: The case of quadraphonic sound, unpublished manuscript, UCLA, 1988.

Prahalad, C. K., A note on the personal computer industry, unpublished case study, University of Michigan, 1983.

Prahalad, C. K., A note on the video camera industry—1984, unpublished case study, University of Michigan, 1984.

Quinn, J., Managing innovation, *Harvard Business Review*, May/June 1985.

Quinn, J., IBM: The System/360 decision. In Quinn, J., H. Mintzberg, and R. James (eds), *The Strategy Process*, Prentice-Hall, Englewood Cliffs, N. J., 1988.

Rae, J. B., *The American Automobile: A brief history*, University of Chicago Press, Chicago, 1965.

Rohlfs, J., A theory of interdependent demand for a communications service, *Bell Journal of Economics*, Spring 1974.

Rosenberg, E., Standards and industry self-regulation, *California Management Review*, Fall 1976.

Rosenbloom, R. S. and M. A. Cusumano, Technological pioneering and competitive advantage: The birth of the VCR industry, *California Management Review*, Summer 1987.

Rumelt, R., The microsoftware industry in 1984, unpublished case study, UCLA, 1985.

S.A.E., *Fortune*, August 1948.

Saloner, G., Economic issues in computer interface standardization, unpublished MIT manuscript, 1989.

Schelling, T. C., *Micromotives and Microbehaviour*, Norton, New York, 1978.

Scherer, F. M., *Industrial Market Structure and Economic Performance*, 2nd edn. Rand McNally, Chicago, 1980.

Sculley, J., *Odyssey*, Harper and Row, New York, 1987.

Shenefield, J., Standards for standards-makers, unpublished address to the American National Standards Institute, 1978.

Shepard, A., Licensing to enhance demand for new technologies, *Rand Journal of Economics*, Autumn 1987.

Sirbu, M. and S. Stewart, Market structure and the emergence of standards: A test in the modem market, unpublished manuscript, 1985.

Sirbu, M. and L. Zwimpfer, Standards setting for computer communication: The case of X.25, *IEEE Communications Magazine*, March 1985.

Smith, P. H., *Wheels within Wheels*, Funk and Wagnalls, New York, 1968.

Stigler, G., The theory of economic regulation, *The Bell Journal of Economics*, Spring 1971.

Swann, G., Industry standard microprocessors and the strategy of second-source supply. In Gabel, L. (ed.), *Product Standardization and Competitive Strategy*, North Holland, Amsterdam, 1987.

Thompson, G., Intercompany technical standardization in the early American automobile industry, *Journal of Economic History*, Winter 1954.

Veall, M., On product standardization as competition policy, *Canadian Journal of Economics*, May 1985.

Yoffie, D., World VTR industry, unpublished Harvard University case study, 1987.

Young, J., Effects of standards on information technology R & D: Local area networks and integrated services digital networks, unpublished manuscript, 1983.

Subject and Company Index

Name Index